SALT O' LIFE

HOWARD MURRY

SALT
O'
LIFE

*with reproductions
of the author's water colors*

1961
JOHN F. BLAIR, *Publisher*
Winston-Salem

TO
The bold spirit of the pioneers
who settled in our Southern mountains
with a lament that
this spirit languishes
and a prayer that it may revive

PREFACE

In the summer of 1932 when the country was in the depth of the great depression, banks closed, commercial life dried up, I deemed it a good time to satisfy a desire I had long had, so I took a sabbatical in a charming rural valley in the North Carolina mountain country.

The place, the simple life, the kindly people, all took hold of me so firmly that I subsequently bought a small piece of land and erected a log cabin on it for a summer place. With changing circumstances brought by time's passage, a day came when I renounced the life of the city and took up a new life in Dutch Cross as a permanent resident.

There are a small number of fine farms along the river and creek bottoms where the soil is rich, but the region is largely a rugged terrain and many of the inhabitants make their living on land so steep it hardly seems possible. It is not an easy life for them, but hard life develops character. The life of these people has few frills, but they plod along and seem even more content and better satisfied than do many other people who encounter less arduous conditions and have more of material possessions.

It soon became apparent to me that the saving grace was humor and a keen appreciation on the part of the people of the small everyday drolleries of life. I think of an occasion back in the days when I lived in the city. A good friend came into the broker's office where I was sitting one morning. He was chuckling to himself at a great rate. Upon my asking him what he was so pleased about he replied:

"I don't believe I could endure life were it not for the small ridiculous things that happen. A man has to have things to laugh at. That is the salt of life. Nina [his wife] drove me down this morning. She turned on the talk as soon as I got in the car, and didn't stop all the way down. As I stepped out of the car I heard her say, 'Don't you think so, Joe?' I said, 'Honey, I don't know. I didn't hear a damn word you said.' "

In this book I am presenting to you something of the "salt" of life which I have gathered in the years I have lived here. It has been good fun gathering it, fun to pass out small grains of it to my friends, and now, more fun to relive it all in the assembling and presenting of it to you.

We live in uneasy, troublesome times, and I think all of us, whatever channels our lives may flow in, are in need of "salt" more than ever before, certainly in my time. The finest, fattest cattle in high-flung mountain pastures would soon sicken and die without their periodic ration of salt. On more than one occasion while I have been sitting on my stool sketching, a cow has sneaked up behind me and rubbed its rasp of a tongue across the back of my neck to taste the salt in my perspiration.

Of course we don't want too much salt all at one time, so I have tried to do up this mountain "salt" for you in small packets, which you may take a little at a time.

HOWARD MURRY

CONTENTS

UNCLE HARD'S COURTIN'   3

PASSIN' THE TIME O' DAY   9

THE MONEY LAUNDRESS   13

VANITY   17

CORN JUICE   23

THE TRESPASSING JACKASS   27

A MOVE TO KAINTUCKY   31

A LONG MEMORY   36

DEMOCRACY   40

BILL FLAGG'S MILL   43

SOWING & REAPING   47

THE GOOD ANGEL   52

TREASURE   56

FECUNDITY   60

A FORETHOUGHTED MAN   63

I HEAR TELL OF UNCLE OLD   65

THE HASTILY DEPARTING GUESTS   69

POINT OF VIEW   73

WAR & PEACE   76

HOT STUFF   80

THE PURPLE SOW	85
A VISIT TO UNCLE OLD	90
ST. PAUL & FARMER PAUL	97
THE KEEN SALESMAN	100
SCHOLARSHIP	103
PAINTING & NEIGHBORING	105
SPIRITS, ANIMAL & GRAIN	111
TESTING THE TELEPHONE	116
A PIONEER SEES THE SIGHTS	119
HOG RIFLES	122
WATER	127
CONNIVANCE?	130
PROOF PERFECT	133
WIPING OUT A FEUD	137
A HILLBILLY HILL CLIMBER	140
FOOTGEAR	143
CURTAIN	146

SALT O' LIFE

Uncle Hard's Courtin'

On a fine Spring morning I drove up Beech Mountain over a road that became progressively worse. It finally became so bad I had my choice of turning around or proceeding afoot. Edging the car into a possible turning place, I picked up easel and paint box and went on by man's original means of travel. Rounding a bend through the trees, I soon came to a small clearing where stood a weatherbeaten log cabin surrounded by a rived picket fence. Gorgeous flowers grew along the fence, and on one side of the cabin an ancient apple tree, half dead, seemed to writhe in the pains of old age. A sunlit crest rose behind the cabin, and, in dramatic contrast, a deep dark purple cloud with wind-torn edges scurried behind it. A scrawny woman carrying a water bucket came out of the cabin door.

"Good morning, Ma'am," said I. "I would like to paint your house if you don't mind."

"Why Mister," she said, "I don't mean to be nowise oncivil, but that there cabin were built by Gran'fer an' his least boy nigh on to a hun'erd years ago an' ain't never had nary drap o' paint on h'it, an' I reckon h'it'll stand another hun'erd without no paint."

Upon my explaining that I merely wanted to paint a picture of it, she quickly agreed, even though she didn't see "ary bit o' sense in h'it."

Setting up my easel I enthusiastically set to work and in a short time completed my sketch pretty well to my satisfaction. Dismounting my easel and packing my paint box, I became aware of a man approaching. He was a plump, jovial-looking fellow, clad in the customary dress of the mountain men, blue overalls, gray work shirt and a battered black hat that almost seemed to grow on top of his head.

"Howdy Sir," said he, "what air ye a'doin'? Makin' a map?" meanwhile closely examining my sketch.

I explained that I was an artist and liked to paint old-time things like his cabin. Raising his head he shouted at his wife, "Come here, Old Woman, an' see what this feller done."

Out she came, wiping her hands on her apron,

and peered inquiringly at my painting. Following a close inspection she spoke:

"Well I'll declare, he sho' has got h'it. There's that twisty ole apple tree, the leanin' outhouse, them flowers an' chickens. H'it's so natural lookin', an say, h'its purty. I never knowed h'it was purty here."

Now I was warmly pressed to come in "an' eat dinner—there's a pot o' beans been a'boilin' ever sence breakfus'." I said I guessed I'd better hurry off. The rejoinder to that was, "Hurry? Why, don't you know a man will overrun a heap more'n he'll ever overtake?"

Such wisdom couldn't be denied, so in we went and sat down to a good hearty dinner, at the end of which my host and I withdrew to the porch, I to fill and light my pipe, he to bite off a huge chew of tobacco. He said to me:

"Mister, you say you like to see and hear about old-timey things?"

"Yes," said I, "I sure do."

"Well," said he, "thish yer cabin ain't no young-un. The woman's gran'fer an' one o' his boys, Hard, put her up a hun'erd years ago. Look at them logs an' them puncheons, how they have hilt out. Folks cain't git that kind of timber no more.

"That Uncle Hard was a turble good hand to

foller most any kind o' doin's, specially raisin' log
walls an' notchin' the corners. See God, Mister, that
man was a character!

"One night he was a'courtin' a gal up at the head
o' Beaver Creek. When h'it come time to go home
an' he started out the door, he seen h'it had gone
to snowin' big, so the gal's pap an' mam tole him he
mus' stay all night. O'course that suited Hard jus'
fine. Well, them people lived in a one-room log
house, jus' like thish yer one, with a lean-to kitchen-
like on one end. The women fixed Hard a bed back
at that kitchen end, the gal clim' the ladder to the
loft, her pap banked the farr an' blowed out the
light, while Hard kicked off his boots, drapped his
britches, an' clim' into the muley bed had been
fixed for him. He kep' his shirt on. Hit were a home-
spun an' hand-wove 'un his mammy had made for
him, out o' flax growed right at home. The women
done that all the time in them days. That afternoon
Hard's mammy had washed an' arned that shirt. In
the time o' arnin', some kine o' racket broke out
among the young-uns out in the yard, an' Hard's
mam had to fly out there to settle h'it. She had lef'
the arn a'settin' on the shirt tail, an' when she come
back toreckly, that there arn were so hot h'it had

burned h'its way plumb through the shirt tail. But
Hard had wore that shirt anyhow, 'cause in them
days sich shirts was made so long they come right
down to a man's knees. So you can see the burned
arn hole bein' so fur down on the tail, h'it come
way below his belt an' didn' make no difference
noway.

"Hard was about to drap off to sleep when h'it
come to his mine that, the bed bein' right alongside
o' the cookin' arrangements, he mus' git up in the
mornin' afore them women come back there an' got
to cookin'.

"The next thing he knowed was a turble jinglin' o'
pots an' kittles, an' there was the women, right
alongside o' him a'makin' breakfus. See God, Mister!
He was sure bothered. He lay there a'figurin' an'
soon see all he could do was throw them quilts back,
jump over the foot board, an' jerk them pants up
rale quick-like.

"He'd a'done good 'cept fur that muley bed. You
know a muley bed has post-es, but them post-es
ain't very high, not at the foot noway, bein' not
much above a man's waist. Well Sir, as Hard went
a'sailin' over that footboard, like a buzzard over the
mounting, his shirt tail a'standin' out behind him

jus' like a bird tail, that there burned arn hole drapped right down over one o' them post-es, an' Hard drug that bed clean to 'tother end o' the house; an' him bein' always a leetle short-like feller, the gal's pap an' mam had to lif' him up off'n that pos'.

"H'it were jus' too funny to the gal's pap to let h'it die out, so he tole about h'it all among the neighbors, an' a'braggin' turble about that shirt Hard's mam had wove that were strong as mule harness. So for years atter that, when the fellers seen Hard a'comin' they'd holler, 'Gee, Haw, Whoa Back.'

"Well Sir, Mister," my host said, "I hate to name h'it to ye, but I'm jus' obliged to hoe out that little 'bacca patch. H'its my money bank. We-uns are po' folks, but we don't mean no harm, an' any time you come back, an'll stay all night, we'll treat you mighty clever."

Assuring him they would see me again soon, I made my way back down to the car, with warm thoughts of "King Hal" and his woman. He was always "King Hal" to me, rotund, a red face with little purple veins, jolly as a sandboy, and a natural-born story-teller if I ever saw one.

Passin' the Time o' Day

I visited in Washington last week. Although the time was pleasurably spent, it is good to be back in my valley once more, where life seems to flow much more evenly and smoothly. On my visits to large cities I am ever struck anew at the vast gulf between the way of life there and our more measured way of life here in the mountains. The city dweller awakes and peers out his window through smog, smoke, and exhaust fumes and sees brick and concrete canyons, asphalt pavings, iron fences, his ears assailed by an unceasing roar of traffic carrying early workers to their jobs. He hurriedly bathes, dresses, gulps his breakfast with a solemn air, thinking of the day's tasks lying ahead of him, and unseeingly dashes off to his work. If he chances to pass a friend on the way, there is only time for a brief nod.

And so through the day, hurrying scurrying, and all amid uproar and confusion.

How is it in Dutch Cross? I came half awake this morning to the murmur of a morning wind in the big white pine outside my window. Quail were calling from the meadow. There are no clocks or schedules pushing me, so not until I feel inclined do I slide out of the bed and proceed to the bathroom, pausing on my way to observe through the window that the row of daffodils lining the drive have come into bloom. There's a golden sun shining. Hanging Rock's head is still blanketed in the cloud that covered him in the night. Now for coffee, in the making of which I bear in mind Fate McCoy's saying, "H'it don't take near as much water to make good coffee as some folks think." Breakfast over, I fill my pipe and go down to the post office for the early mail.

Joe Nutley was sitting out in front smoking his pipe. He keeps that pipe going just about all day long every day. Presently old Uncle Ben Crow came along to get his mail. Joe is a strong "Bab-dis," while Uncle Ben is an equally strong Episcopalian. The following exchange took place:

Joe: "Howdy Ben, how you doin'?"

Ben: "Ain't doin' no good. How you doin'?"

JOE: "About like common."

BEN: "I been a'goin' to the Episcopal convention up at the Mission School. Bishop there and nine priests. I sure been enjoyin' h'it."

JOE: "Huh, I don't know which I'd ruther be caught at, a Episcopal convention or a nigger frolic."

BEN: "Well, I expect h'it would depend on a man's raisin'."

BYSTANDERS: "Haw, haw, haw."

A fresh breeze was blowing, and Joe was having difficulty relighting his pipe.

BEN: "I declare Joe, never see a man smoke as much as you do. Don't you know even a hog don't use no tobacca?"

JOE: "Who does that make most like a hog Ben, you or me?"

George Allison spoke up: "Speakin' o' hogs, you-uns know that new farm manager at the Mission School? Well, yestiddy I were a'settin' on the porch at Charl Turner's a'talkin' to him, an' that feller come in at the gate, walked up to Charl an' said, 'We got to do somethin' about them hogs o' yourn. They been through the fence an' in my corn agin.' Charl says, 'Why Son, I never knowed a little corn to hurt a hog.' "

"That Charl is a smart feller," Orville Hilton said. "They ain't nobody gets by better on less work than he does. 'Tother day him an' his brother Hoke was a'workin' down in his lower medder. When I come along they had quit an' were a'layin' under a shade tree by the fence. I retch in my pocket, pulled out a quarter, hilt h'it up an' said, 'If I knowed which one of you fellers was the laziest, I'd give him this two bits.' Hoke helt out his hand an' said, 'Give her here.' That Charl never moved. Jus' said, 'Drop her in my pocket Son.'"

Then I had one to tell on Charl. Yesterday I went up to his house to see him and was met at the door by one of his girls. She was wreathed in smiles, said she knew just where to find him. A few minutes before I came she had gone up to her grandmother's room and "had found Papa sitting in a rocking chair smoking his pipe. I asked him what in the world he was doing there all by himself. His answer was, 'Just a'hidin' from your mama Honey. She don't give me no rest.'"

I suppose none of us will rake in many dollars today, but we have gotten ourselves in good shape to undertake the day's tasks, and the group disperses in various directions.

The Money Laundress

On one of my favorite drives, which completely encircles the Beech Mountain, there is a large two-story white house. There is a porch all around the front and on one side, and over the side porch there is also an upper porch. I would always marvel at the fact that there were fifteen or twenty bee gums on the upper porch. Passing there one day last week, I saw an elderly man in the yard with a rake in his hand. I stopped and spoke to him, introducing myself. He gave me his name, Sloan Hammond, and invited me to come sit on the porch. His wife came out, and I was properly introduced to her.

I said to him that I had long wondered what made a man keep bee gums on his upper porch, and asked if he would please satisfy my curiosity.

"Why," he said, "I just love to lay in bed of a hot night below that porch an' listen at the bees a'fannin' the honey with their wings to keep it from heatin'."

Finding that Mr. Hammond sold honey, I bought a jar and in payment tendered a dog-eared and very dirty dollar bill, apologizing for its condition. Whereupon he said:

"That dirty bill reminds me of somethin' happened a long time ago. I've been a turble hand most of my life to log an' sawmill. I cut thousands of feet of timber off most of these mountains round here. I used to sell it mostly to mills over in Tennessee. Some of it was rafted down creeks and rivers, an' some hauled by ox teams, though roads was few and turble rough. I'd generally ship for a month, then saddle a horse an' go see them fellers to collect. I'd git the pay in cash, 'cause that's the way I had to pay my hands an' buy most of my supplies. This time I'm tellin' you about I'd been over there collectin' an' had about seven hundred dollars in my clothes. It was in winter, an' cold as whiz, January, I believe it was. Aimin' to cut the journey some, an' git in home soonest, I decided to undertake a near cut I had never tried. It run for a good way up a rough gorge. Of course I was a'horseback, 'cept every now an' then I would have to git off an' walk a spell to keep the blood a'goin'. Well, we come to a ford. It looked all right, though a right smart of ice along the river edges. We got most across, the water about up to the horse's belly, an' a pretty bold current, when that horse caught a forefoot. He struggled an' struggled but couldn't git a'loose, so there was nothin' else for it 'cept to slide off his back an' try to holp him git loose. What happened was he had wedged his foot in a big old sunken forked limb. By the Lord's holp, an' a'pullin' an' a'tuggin', I got that foot a'loose after so long a time, an' we clim' the bank.

"Of course I was soaked an' near about froze. Dark was a'comin' fast an' I didn't know for sure where I was at. Finally I spied a little log house at the head of a holler, with smoke comin' out the chimley. Went to the door an' knocked an' a man opened to me, an' I told him the fix I was in. Well Sir, him an' his woman took me in an' couldn't a'been more clever. He put my horse in the barn, fed him, rubbed him down. He built the fire in the chimley place up big, made me take off my clothes an' hang 'em by the fire, an' lent me some of his.

"In the time of all this the woman had cooked up a fine supper. How I could eat in them days! After supper, bein' wore out, they put me to bed in the next room, leavin' my clothes in the main room to finish dryin' by the fire. I slep' like the dead.

"Next mornin' that man come in my room bringin' my clothes. His woman had ironed 'em, washed my shirt an' underwear, an' made 'em look like Sunday mornin'. Then it come to me about all that money. I hadn't give it no thought when I undressed. I reached in the inner coat pocket where I had left it in a little canvas sack, opened that sack, took them bills out, looked at 'em, an' I was shocked! That woman had washed and ironed all them dirty bills till they looked like they just come out of the mint. An' it was all there, every cent. You reckon folks'd treat a man that-a-way these days?"

Vanity

There is a grand old man I have often heard of who lives over on the Blue Mountain. He is known far and wide as Smiling Sam. In his young days he was driving a horse and wagon one day through a field when the horse stepped in a hornet's nest. The hornets stung him all over and drove him wild. Away he tore over that rough field and in a short time had torn wagon and harness to bits. Sam was badly hurt, having been thrown out on a rock pile. He lay in hospital for weeks, finally recovering fairly well except for his legs, which were partially paralyzed and of little use to him. The doctor finally dismissed him, confessing he could do nothing further for Sam, but at the same time expressing his belief that there was a certain operation could be done at Johns Hopkins in Baltimore that might give him the re-use of his legs. Certain letters were written and it developed that there was indeed hope. However, Sam found to his dismay that a considerable sum of money would be required, while by now all his funds were gone.

Holding a sublime faith, and determined to go to any necessary lengths, and with no other means available, he borrowed money from half a dozen well-known men in the county, and promising to make every penny good, he left for Baltimore.

In a few weeks, the operation over, and well along the road toward complete recovery, Sam came home. He worked, slaved, saved, denying himself everything not essential, and in a few years paid back all the money he had borrowed.

A few days ago I drove over on The Blue to explore painting possibilities, and then went to call on Smiling Sam. I introduced myself, we sat down and he said to me:

"Son, you come at jus' the right time. I jus' got back from a funeral. My Goodness, how them folks was dressed up, specially the women! Why one of 'em had a young-un, a boy about half growed, got somethin' wrong with his neck, has to wear a arn brace from his shoulders to the top o' his head; an' do you know that woman had tied a blue ribbon bow on that there arn brace! Vanity, vanity, all is vanity.

"H'it puts me in mine of a family used to live down the river cross over on t'other side, family name o' Rupert. That man had the best o' everythin', fine river bottom farm, fat stock, big fine horses, the best bull in the county, a big stand o' virgin timber, jus' about all a body could want.

"He had him a good woman an' three fine gals, an' of a Sunday when they went to preachin' there wan't no finer dressed woman persons in the county. When Rupert went anywheres, though, folks kinely shied away from him. They didn' care to hear his unendin' braggin' about all he had.

"Of a Sunday when h'it come time to go to preachin', that man would hitch up not one, but two teams o' the finest, fattest dapple grays you ever seen, puttin' one team in front o' t'other, four-in-hands I reckon you call 'em. An' them people didn' set on no plain boards for seats. No Sir, they put cheers in that wagon, an' cushions in them cheers, so they always come to the church house door in the finest style.

"There was a feller lived on down the river a

piece, kine of a shiftless, no-count feller. Long ganglin' man, no meat on his bones, neck like a turkey, an' he were as freckled as a mounting trout. Folks all called him Speckles. He were a widder man, didn' have no woman, hunted an' fished a heap, done a little farmin'. He didn' have no horse, jus' a big ole brindle ox. That feller come to church regular, an' mos'ly he'd come without no shoes, him bein so po', an' not carin' noways.

"Speckles jus' couldn' stand seein' them Ruperts arrivin' in all that style, them fine four horses an' all, an' he give the matter a heap o' thought. Him, he'd come to church on that brindle ox's back, saddle, bridle an' all, his ole bare feet a'hangin' down an' most touchin' the groun'. He grumbled a heap about folks who put on airs.

"One day a'workin' Ole Brindle, Speckles give him a accidental poke right back of where the foreleg grows out o' the body. Talk about a ticklish girl! That ox bellered, rared up, an' carried on. The great idea was borned in Speckles' mine. Every day or so he would work on that tickle spot to keep Ole Brindle in trainin'.

"Come Sunday, Spec shaved, fixed up, an' put out for church, o'course ridin' Ole Brindle. Now the

road from Spec's cabin comes off the hill an' runs
into the road from Rupert's farm near about in front
o' the church house. At the meetin' place o' the two
roads, there's a thick stand o' hemlocks. Well Sir,
Spec rides up to them hemlocks, an' waits till he
hears a team a'comin' down that other road an'
would peep out to see who it was.

"When he seen the Ruperts a'comin', at jus' the
right moment, he forces Ole Brindle through them
pines, touches that tickle spot with his great ole
long bare toe. O'course Brindle let out a beller an'
riz up right under the lead horses' noses. Mister, you
ain't never seen nothin'! Them horses done everythin' a horse can do. They stood on their hind legs,
stepped over traces, struck one another comin'
down, an' then they run. The women folks squealed
an' tumbled out'a the wagon a'fore the runnin'
started. Ole Man Rupert stuck to the lines an' tried
to guide them horses into the church house to stop
'em. They missed h'it by a hair bit an' tore aroun'
the back corner o' the church house. They was two
privies behine, one for women an' one for men. They
was only about five foot betwixt 'em. Them horses
headed right for that gap. O'course the singletrees
caught on them two johnnies, an' they was drug to

the edge o' them big woods, where them horses was obliged to stop.

"Now you can believe h'it or not Mister, jus' as you please, the preacher's sermon that day was all about the evil o' vanity."

I drove homeward with visions of that four-horse team careening into the privies, and Speckles, astride his ox, engulfed in laughter. Smiling Sam is indeed a valuable addition to my list of new friends. I must see him again soon, to say nothing of Miss Georgia, his sister. She's ninety-two years old and cute as a bug's ear.

Corn Juice

M any of the people of our community receive most of their year's income at near the end of the year, harvest time. As a consequence the store through much of the year sells largely on credit. In winter and on rainy days many of the same group sit around the huge stove and swap news and ideas, gossip and tell stories. As most of the sitters are "on the books," the group has not unnaturally acquired the dignity of the name, the "Jot-'Em-Down Club."

Day before yesterday I was attending a session of the club when Roy Sleek came in and joined us. Roy is mostly legs, the length of them largely making up his six and a half feet of height, and he carries a tiny head perched on a long scrawny neck. Roy informed us that he had just returned from the county seat, and having some time to kill, had sat in the court house listening to trials. He proceeded to regale us with the following account:

"Boys, that last case was somethin'. They had a feller up for bootleggin'. All the evidence was clear agin' him, an' the jury had to fine him guilty. The judge tole the feller to stan' up to be sentenced. That bootlegger is a smart, slickery kine of a feller. Well, up he jumps like he were a'goin' to a frolic, an' says, 'Yes Sir, Judge.' You'd'a thought he was doin' the judge a favor. The judge says, 'I'm a'goin' to let you off light, two hundred dollars fine.' 'Yes Sir, Judge,' the feller says, 'I got h'it right here in my pocket,' pullin' out a great ole big wad o' bills. Folks kinely snickered. The judge raps with that wooden mallet o' his an' says, 'An', six months on the road gang. Have you got that in your pocket too?' Them folks in the court house sho' did laugh.

"I know where that bootlegger gets most o' his stuff. I ain't a'goin' to name the shiner, but don't care to tell you he lives in a wild-like place up on Long Hope. He's a ole feller an' has been stillin' for ten years I know of, an' there don't never nobody bother his still. H'it's in a ole log house with a great ole big rock chimley an' sets right in the middle of a ten-acre field up on one of them big balds. He

keeps a good fence all round h'it, an' all the time
he keeps two of the meanest bulls in h'it you ever
seen. They beats ary guard dog you ever heerd of.

"I'll tell you how I got on to him. 'Bout ten year
ago I were up in them parts a'loggin'. One Sunday,
climbin' over that ridge, I met up with a feller I
knowed. I had a yaller raincoat on my arm. That
feller seen h'it, liked h'it, an' wanted to trade me out
o' h'it. I didn' want to let h'it go, so that feller pulls
out a quart bottle of white likker, and we takes us
a dram. Boys, that were the best likker I ever
knowed! I kinely praised h'it some, so the feller says
he'd trade me the balance of h'it for the raincoat,
that he didn' want no more likker noways. So I done
that, give him the coat, an' took the likker.

"We sit on a log an' talked a spell, an' I kep'
a'takin' a dram, the feller not takin' no more. By an'
by I 'lowed I mus' git on in an' eat supper, as I were
gittin' kinely hongry.

"I reckon I made about three hundred yards,
feelin' fine, an' my mine jes' as clear as that little
spring back o' my barn, when all of a sudden my
laigs turn't to water, an' down I went. I tried a time
or two but jes' couldn' stan', so I give up an' went to
sleep in them big ole woods.

"Atter so long a time I waked, mine still plumb clear as spring water, an' them laigs some better, though still kinely weak-like. I made h'it on in to that house where we was a'stayin', an' somehow h'it come to my mine to look up the sign in the almanac, an' Boys, what do you spose? The sign was in the laigs!

"That likker come from that bull pen still I was a'tellin' about."

Frank Morse said:

"Roy, it's good the sign wasn't in the head. If it had been, you'd a'been drunk sure enough!"

The Trespassing Jackass

Our country store at Dutch Cross is a fine old-fashioned one where one can buy almost anything a reasonable man might want. I even bought a pair of ox shoes there one day and used them in a coffee table I was building, the shoes having a certain decorative quality. In the middle of the store there is a remarkable old-time stove about seven feet high, and all around the stove a ring of limber "settin' cheers." On rainy days and in winter the "cheers" are pretty well all occupied, and one can hear all manner of talk, most of it good, for the mountain man is not overly articulate and seems to have less trouble than most of us in suppressing foolish, senseless thoughts. There are professional discussions of Bible passages, politics, the stock market (the kind one keeps in pastures, not bank vaults); of course, too, crops and weather must be fully dealt with, and there is plenty of seasoning in the way of stories, which for the most part are humorous.

One windy, rainy day this week there was a group of us sitting around the stove drinking "sody pop," smoking, chewing, and "dipping," when Holston Webber came in. One could always rely upon Holston for a laugh. Protocol demands that upon coming into the store one must first sit and "neighbor" and then do one's trading, so, of course, Holston joined the group and sat down on a nail keg. Conversation had lagged, and most of us looked at him expectantly.

"Boys," he said, "you-uns know that jackass of Joe Smith's [a neighbor of Holston's] that I been a'fussin' about him a'comin' over in my garden? Well, I think I got him fixed.

"One mornin' las' month me an' the woman was a'eatin' breakfus an' I seen out the winder them ole long ears a'stickin' up in my patch of roas'n years. I called two of the boys, an' we run him out of thar an' hemmed that brute up in a fence corner. Then I went to the barn an' got me a set of harness, slapped h'it on that critter, hitched him to the sled, an' drove him to that patch of new groun' me an' the boys are clearin'. We'd pile that sled up with stumps an' rocks an' make that critter haul 'em off. Never in life did a jackass have such a mass of work put on him. We kep' him at h'it til near dark, then I unhooked, took the harness off him, slapped him on the hine quarters, an' Boys, did he take off! I ain't seen him sence, an' I ain't a'goin' to, 'cause that critter is too smart to git luxuries he has to pay fur."

Fred Patrick spoke up and said:

"Boys, I can tell you some more about that same dang jackass. He died out yestiddy. I reckon he had been a'livin' too high on folks's roas'n years. I can laugh about h'it now, though h'it didn' seem so funny in the time of h'it.

"I met Joe in the road about dinner time yestiddy, an' he tole me about h'it a'dyin'. I had to git funny an' ask him when would the funeral be. He said he didn' know yit but would let me hear as soon as he knowed for sure.

"Well, I went on in the house, eat dinner an' forgot all about h'it. Las' night atter supper I was tard, as I'd had a hard day, so I hit the hay soon atter eatin'. In the night there come a heavy bangin' an' knockin' at the door downstairs. I made me a light an' seen h'it were one o'clock. I stuck my head out the winder an' hollered down, 'Who's thar? What's happened?' H'it were Joe Smith. He said, 'Fred, come down. I got to see you a minute.' I slipped on my britches, stuck my feet in my shoes, an' a'carryin' the lamp, went to the door an' let Joe in. What do you reckon that monkey said to me? He says:

" 'Fred, I promised to let you know as soon as I knowed when that jackass funeral is to be, an' I aim to keep my promise. I done decided to have it tomorrow at two, an' you bein' sich a good neighbor, I want you to be one of the pallbearers.' "

A Move to Kaintucky

Sunday afternoons in the country you go visit someone, or visitors come to see you, and you catch up on what's going on in the county. At church this morning I saw a lady and her husband who have a near-by summer place. I called on them last night. When I saw them this morning they spoke some courteous words of appreciation of my visit, and then the lady added, "And I am so glad you came at night, instead of during the day. If these people around here would make their visits at night, instead of staying home and going to bed so early, they wouldn't have so many children."

I followed the usual pattern this afternoon and drove up the mountain to visit with "King Hal" and his wife. Miss Eliza was sitting on the porch snapping beans. The "King" had gone across the mountain to see a neighbor man about maybe swapping

labour. I was disappointed over his absence, as I
was hoping to hear another good story from him.

At Miss Eliza's invitation to "hev a cheer," I sat
down in a settin' cheer. The man who designed
these "settin' cheers" was a wonderful fellow. He
certainly knew the shape of the human body and
how to fit it comfortably. Put together as they are,
without nails or screws, they will give service for
a hundred years or more, with a new "bottom"
occasionally.

Miss Eliza sat in another such "settin' cheer." On
a small table beside her was a pan of beans and a
can of snuff. Her "toothbrush" stuck out from one
side of her mouth, and a tin can at her feet did
service as a cuspidor.

To start conversation going, I asked a not unusual
polite question in the mountains, "Who was your
daddy, Miss Eliza?"

"Lee Storm," she replied. "He come from down
in the valley, at Dutch Cross. That's where my
gran'maw was raised at. I don't care to tell you that
nobody knowed who her folks was. My great-
gran'paw was a'workin' in his medder one day,
when he heerd a puny little cryin' amongst a patch
o' tall daisies on the creek bank. He looked down

in thar an' seen a leetle newborn baby. H'it were a
gal chile. He picked that baby up an' carried her to
the house. They never could learn nothin' about
who left her there, or nothin', so they kep' her an'
raised her. On account of her bein' found amongst
them daisies a'growin' in the medder, they named
her Daisy Medders, an' that was my gran'maw.

"When she growed up, Gran'paw kep' a'beggin'
her to marry him. Now remember, they was a'livin'
down below the mounting at Dutch Cross. Them
people down there was always good to her, but I
reckon Gran'maw never did feel right a'knowin'
that everybody knowed she was a woods chile. So
h'it come to her one day to tell Gran'paw she'd
agree to marry him if he would take her to Kaintucky to live. He didn' care to do that, him bein'
young an' stout, so they went an' got the preacher
an' he tied the knot.

"The very next day they put out for Kaintucky.
Gran'paw had a leetle spotted ox, an' they packed
their few belongin's on that ox's back—folks didn'
have much in them days—an' started a'walkin' up
Valley Mounting.

"Well Sir, they trudged them rough tracks an'
trails for several days, over them mountings, an'

down through leetle valleys, stayin' of a night with
folks along the way. In them days there wasn't nobody hardly would turn a person away of a night.

"One fine mornin' Gran'paw tole her, 'We are
now in Kaintucky.' They went on a piece an' come
up on a bunch o' men a'loggin', an' a'sawin' up them
logs, an' a'hewin' 'em up into crossties for the railroad. The work boss got to talkin' to Gran'paw an'
wanted to know could he do good with a broadaxe.
Gran'paw owned he could, so that man give him a
job. He got fifty cents a day, which wan't bad pay
in them days.

"Well Sir, the years went by an' the Lord was
good to 'em. Gran'paw had worked out enough
money to buy him this leetle farm an' built this very
cabin where we set. They was eleven young-uns, an'
they didn' but three of 'em died out afore they was
growed.

"Gran'maw had one special favorite leetle cow
brute she was turble fond of. One night when she
went up to the milk gap to do her milkin', that leetle
cow brute failed to come in with the balance of 'em.
Next mornin' that leetle cow again failed to show
up. So, atter she got her chores done up, her an' the
least 'un put off acrost them high mounting pastures
to hunt her. About mid-atternoon they hadn't had

no luck an' was about to give up an' come in when she heerd a faint-like jingle of a cowbell. H'it seemed to come from down below a big rock clift jus' ahead of 'em. They moved up closter so Gran'-maw could hear better, an' lo, h'it were onmistakable. That were that ole cowbell her pap had made one day when Gran'maw was a young-un. H'it had kinely come apart at the joint, which give h'it a most onusual kine of a sound, not like ary other cowbell a body ever heerd. There was some great ole big laurel bushes growed up at the clift edge. Pushin' 'em apart, an' a'peerin' through 'em, she seen right down there in the valley her pap's farm. H'it wan't more'n half a mile away, an' all them twenty years or more she had thought she was a'livin' in Kaintucky.

"So, you can't never tell. There's some o' them folks down below the mounting a'cavortin' aroun' in autymobiles, an' a'dancin', an' a'goin' to picture shows, an' think they are a'livin' in Heaven. H'it may be they are as clost to Hell as Gran'maw was to her pap's all them years."

I debated with myself all the way home, which is more important? Where you are, or where you think you are?

A Long Memory

Among my neighbors at Dutch Cross is an elderly
man, Charles Turner, who has successfully
farmed and traded in the neighborhood all his life.
"Charl" is known and loved throughout the countryside. He has a keen sense of humor and is full of
recollections and stories. He lives on the place next
to me, so we often see each other. I went to see him
this morning and found him walking around the
room looking on shelves, tables, the floor, ever and
anon searching his pockets. I enquired what had
been lost:

"Sarnall Son, I can't find my pipe. Don't know
what went with it. It's got so my memory ain't worth
a cent any more."

I happened to have a cigar in my pocket, so I
handed him that, and he led the way to two comfortable rockers on the porch.

"Speakin' of memory," said he, "reminds me of Sam Short. Sam was born and raised over on Timber Ridge, in the Stone Mountain country. Sam's pappy, Old Tom, was a straight, hard-workin' feller, terrible religious, but bad tempered. When he flew mad his rage went through him like fire through a timber boundary in dry times, an' a East wind a'blowin'.

"One time Old Tom was a'fixin' to split some chestnut fence rails. He was a'huntin' all through the shed an' the barn for his maul an' couldn't find it nowhere, when it come to him that a neighbor, lived about two mile away, had borrowed it an' had failed to bring it back, so he called Sam an' told him to go over an' get that maul, an' hurry up. So Sam was off, and after so long a time come to the man's house an' told him what he wanted. The man says, 'Why Son, if I've got it, you'll find it in the woodshed. God knows it's trouble enough to borrow stuff, let alone return it.' So that boy hunted an' hunted, an' the man come an' holp him, but they just couldn't find it. Finally, there bein' nothin' else to do, that boy went on in home an' told his pa how it was.

"Old Tom raley flew mad when Sam told him.

He cut him a mean hick'ry an' give Sam a turble whippin'. He near about wore that hick'ry out. Now Sam was right big of a boy, about sixteen I reckon, an' he decided he just couldn't go on livin' at home no more, with his pappy mean like that. So that night he tied up his few duds in a old shirt, slipped out the back door, an' nobody heerd no tell of him for years atter that.

"What happened was, that boy had worked his way clean out to Washington state. He worked hard, went to night school, read law, become a lawyer, got to be raley big, made him a big success.

"About twenty-five years atter he had left home, he had a yearnin' to go back an' see the old home place again. So he packed up, got on the train, an' come into Boone on that little narr gauge railroad from Johnson City. In Boone he hired him a feller with a horse an' buggy to drive him out to the old home place. On the way he stopped at a wheel-wright's, where an old feller made wagons, sleds, an' such-like, an' bought a maul from him. Then they drove on.

"When they got to the house there was Old Tom a'sittin' on the porch, a'readin' his Bible. Sam jumps out the buggy, all diked out in his fine clothes, picks up that maul, walks up to his pappy, slams that maul down on the porch floor at Old Tom's feet, an' says, 'Papa, there's you a damn maul.' "

I had hoped to get the use of Charl's saddle horse and ride over some high pastures, but by now, with one of our sudden changes of weather, rain had started falling, so I had to abandon my project and trudged homeward, wondering whether Sam Short made his success through sheer ambition and ability, or just to score off his papa.

Democracy

Nature has treated our mountain region harshly and cruelly. In my last writing in this journal I had walked home from Charl Turner's in the rain. Rain fell all that day, and all day long every day for three weeks, with a grand finale on the last day, when the rain seemed to pour more heavily than ever. The limit of the earth's ability to absorb water was reached and exceeded. Small creeks and branches became wild roaring rivers. Cattle, sheep, haystacks, houses, barns, roads were torn and swept miles away. In places on the mountains the ground literally exploded and started great landslides. Rocks weighing twenty-five to thirty tons were rolled and pushed as far as half a mile from their beds. There has been much distress and loss, not only of property, but of lives.

I was out painting this morning on Dutchman's Creek. After finishing my sketch and coming back to the car, I met an old woman walking down the road. I "passed the time of day" with her and asked whether she had suffered much damage from the flood.

"Yes Sir, h'it taken everythin' I had 'cept the clothes I'm a'standin' in. Tuck the house—yonder is what h'it lef' of the chimley, tuck the barn, the crops—an' they was awful good uns too; oh! an' h'it tuck my ole man, an' my boy, drownded both of 'em. They didn' fine the man's body till seventy-five miles away down the river, clear over in Tennessee."

I was very much touched by her tale of disaster and enquired whether she had applied to the authorities at the county seat for aid.

"You mean them fellers over at Boone? Yes Sir, I got me a way over there, went in an' tole 'em how it was, answered a whole pile of fool questions, signed a lot of papers, an' never got nothin'. I tell ye, I'm so mad I jus' ain't never goin' to vote no more."

"Ah," said I, "did you vote the last time?"

"Yes Sir."

"Who did you vote for?"

"The one what done the most good."

"What was his name?"

"I don't know. He were the one what done the most good."

"How did you know he was the one that did the most good?"

"Them fellers standin' round the polls said he was, but I ain't takin' that no more. I'll not never vote agin."

Bill Flagg's Mill

Reports of damage by the flood continue to come in from the isolated back country. They are indeed distressing, and those who suffered little or no damage are doing what they can to alleviate the distress of others. I heard of a case this morning that, although it is a story of loss, at the same time has a ridiculously funny side and will bring many a laugh in our community for a long time to come. It deals with Bill Flagg, who lives on Orchard Creek a little way above Dutch Cross.

Bill is a versatile old man and has many ways of bringing in the little he needs to take care of his simple requirements. I once asked him whether he felt that life is much better these days with good roads, automobiles, electricity, etc., than it was in old times. Without hesitation he answered, "No Sir, folks was a heap more contented and satisfied in them old days. They didn' have much, but never knowed the difference, because there wasn't no rich folks aroun' showing off what they had an' makin' po' folks jealous, an' too, folks had time to visit one another an' holp the other man out of a tight." He is quoted as having once said, "Me an' my boys can go to the store an' git ary thing we want, an' pay fur h'it, but we don't want everythin' we see."

Just below Bill's house, on the banks of the creek, the old man had a little water-powered grist mill, and on mill days he did a thriving trade grinding turns of corn for people in the neighborhood. The little mill had been cunningly anchored to the big rocks among which it was built, but finally toward the last day of the rains things were looking terribly grave, and Old Bill had put on his slicker and gone down to the little mill to see how it was faring. He was appalled when he saw how much worse matters had become since his last look.

As he watched, a huge dead chestnut came careening down the stream, crashed into the water wheel, and carried away the broken pieces. Those old-time water wheels were homemade and were

marvels of dexterous workmanship. A long time was
required in the making of them, and it hurt the old
man to his soul to see his wheel smashed and swept
away.

The creek roared like fifty express trains, the
spray so dense everything was veiled. A landslide
erupted above on Valley Mountain, and the rains
seemed to slip into a still higher gear.

Although not a particularly religious man, Old
Bill fell to his knees, clasped his hands, and from his
inner depths burst into prayer.

"Oh Lord, here's Old Bill Flagg a'talkin' to ye.
Have pity upon me Lord, an' don't let my little mill
be washed away. Hear me this one time Lord, an'
I will seldom if ever call upon Thee again. I will not
be like Preacher Loop at the Mission, eternally
ding-dongin' at Thee. I know that Thou didst
promise S. T. Paul that never again wouldst Thou
let the earth be covered up with water, but h'it is
lookin' mighty scrupulous."

About this time the little dam further up the
mountain carried away, and the resultant wall of
water which came smashing down the creek tore
the little mill from its foundations, and down it
went, the pieces tossing in the mad current like wild

horses. Without pause in his impassioned prayer Old Bill concluded:

"Now, by God, Thou hast eternally played Hell with me!"

How did this story get around? Alas! There is no privacy in the country. Whatever you do, the neighbors will know it. Hiram Hammond did some small jobs for me this morning, and it was from him I got the story. He was up the creek looking for one of his cows which had strayed, and which he feared might have drowned. He was standing behind one of those big rocks watching the torrent when Old Bill was making his prayer.

Sowing & Reaping

I have access to a fine trout stream which flows across the back of Sloan Hammond's farm. Yesterday afternoon, feeling no desire to paint, I got out my rod and went down to the Hammonds' to do a bit of fishing. Luck was with me and I am looking forward to a fine supper of brook trout tonight. On my way back to the car, I stopped at the house to report the result of my efforts, to leave a part of the catch, and to express my thanks.

Uncle Sloan was sitting by the empty stove in the bedroom reading his Bible. A rocking chair was pulled out for me, I filled my pipe, and we got comfortable. He said:

"I've just been readin' that good line in the Book, 'As a man soweth, so shall he reap.' It sure is the truth. I ricollect somethin' that happened round here a few years back that sure proves the truth of that sayin'.

"There was a feller lived up at the head of a long holler under Rockyface, him an' his wife, six young-uns, an' his old dad. The feller didn' have much of a livin', just about made it. His old dad was pretty well up in years, an kinely puny-like most of the time, which made him somewhat of a care for the feller an' his woman. Finally it come to the feller that they could maybe get the old pappy in the County Home, so the feller got him a way to Boone, saw the folks had charge of sich-like, an' got the arrangements made without no trouble much.

"The next day the woman packed them a lunch, an' they started out, the feller an' his dad, walkin' an' takin' the near cuts, so's to save distance.

"About halfway they clim' a turble steep hill, Tom's Knob. On top there was a great old big flat rock. It had a most curious colour, sort of a dirty-lookin' white, an' dotted with purple spots about the size of a quarter.

"The old pappy bein' purty tard, they sat 'em down on that rock to rest a spell. The feller, bein' stout, an' anxious to get matters settled, was soon ready to go on agin an' kep urgin' his pappy to come on, but the ole feller still sat. Finally the feller told his daddy they was just obliged to go on, so's he could git back in home in time to git his work done up a'fore dark.

"The old man sighed an' said, 'All right Son. My mine was way back in old days. I was just a'thinkin' how my pappy sat an' rested on this very same rock I'm a'sittin' on when I took him to the County Home.'"

As Uncle Sloan concluded his story, his wife came into the room and urged me to "rest easy an' eat supper with us." There were very fine smells coming from the kitchen of frying ham and strong coffee, so I did not require much urging, and we soon sat down to a delightful meal.

As Uncle Sloan and I sat around the stove after supper—a little fire by now felt good, Miss Lizzie came into the room, a letter in her hand and a bright look on her face. I have found out that Miss Lizzie is an active sower of seeds and is loved and respected for her good deeds throughout that back settlement. She said to me:

"I got a letter today I want to read to you. It made me feel awful good, but first I'll have to tell you what lays back of it.

"We have a heap of awful poor folks livin' round here. Plenty of 'em just ain't got nothin' hardly. There's right many summer visitors comes to these parts, an' some of 'em are so good hearted they keep a'sendin' me things like clothes an' shoes, an' old toys, an' such, for me to pass out to them that's worthy an' needs 'em. Last month a nice lady come from up in Pennsylvania, an' learnin' how things are around here, said her an' the other ladies in her church would send me a fine box of things to hand out for Christmas.

"About three weeks after that lady went home a letter come from her, said she was plumb grieved. Said her an' the other ladies had started fillin' us a box, when one day the pastor ask them, what was the religion of them people down in the Carolina mountings. Of course the lady told him Bab-dis. 'Oh Ladies,' he says, 'I'm sorry, but we can't send them that box. We are Lutherans, an' we got to look after our own.'

"Well, I sat down an' wrote that lady. I told her to never mind that I was just a pore mounting woman an' didn' know no better. Told her I looked round an' seen men in uniforms of the Army, an' the Navy, of the Air Force, an' the Merchant Marine,

of the C.B.'s an' the Red Cross, all of 'em a'fightin'
for an' a'servin' the one cause—the country, an' I
thought it was the same way in fightin' God's cause.

"Now this letter was wrote me by that preacher,
an' I want you to read it." The letter ran:

Dear Mrs. Hammond:

Mrs. P—— has shown me your letter. You have made me
realize a very great divine truth, thereby placing me in
debt to you. I am urging our Ladies Aid Society to send
you the finest box possible for your Christmas distribution
to the needy.

The Good Angel

Last night I was debating with myself how many trout to put in the pan for supper when our clergyman, Mr. Trent, stopped by to give me a message. As his wife is away on a visit, and he is without a housekeeper, it was not difficult to persuade him to stay and have supper with me.

Mr. Trent is a man broadly interested in all sorts of things relating to people, their ways and doings. The psychic, the subconscious, etc., particularly intrigue him. He is widely read in these subjects and can tell many remarkable things. After supper our conversation not unnaturally ranged into the field of his interests.

Mr. Trent's wife is the daughter of a former rector of our parish, a man who spent many years here in loving and devoted service to the community. He was known far and wide throughout the region and generally loved for his fine qualities. He was, withal, a very commonsense practical man, without illusions or fancies, which qualities are also evident in his daughter's make-up.

Our conversation turned to the mysterious forces which seem to play an active part in guiding and impelling people in their various actions, sometimes seeming to guard them, or sometimes seeming to push them into trouble. This led to his telling me of a remarkable experience of Mrs. Trent's and her father's that had befallen about the turn of the century, before the Trents were married.

One day father and daughter were driving down Watauga River. Their conveyance was a horse and buggy, there being no automobiles in these parts at the time. They were proceeding slowly, as it had been raining, and the road was very soft and muddy. The landscape was veiled in a filmy mist.

As they were driving through a patch of woods, a figure appeared coming toward them through the trees, came to them at the side of the buggy, and the horse stopped.

Addressing the clergyman, the figure spoke affirmatively, with no note of questioning in his voice:

"You are going on down river and expecting to cross at John's Ford."

"Yes Sir," replied the minister.

"By no means try to cross the ford," the figure said. "There was a cloudburst up on that little mountain this afternoon, it scoured out the river bottom at the ford, and the depth of water would be over your horse's head."

With that the figure seemed to melt away in the misty woods.

The old gentleman and his daughter looked at each other and marveled. They knew everybody in the county, but there had been nothing familiar about this strange man. His English had been flawless, without any local flavour, his style of dress not that one was accustomed to in these parts. They pondered over the mystery as they drove on but could come to no conclusion.

About three miles down river they came to John's Ford. Everything looked about as usual, but at the edge of the river their horse stopped and simply would not enter the ford. Urging, whipping, nothing would move him.

Night was coming on and they were quite a long way from home. Finally, as there seemed nothing else to do, they turned around and drove back about half a mile to the house of some people they knew well, where they told of their strange experience.

The householders were kindly hospitable people and insisted upon their visitors staying the night, which they were glad to do.

The next morning after breakfast, accompanied by the man of the house, his two sons, and the old grandfather, they drove down to the ford.

The men had taken an axe, and they cut long poles to probe the depth of water in the ford. To their amazement they found that the water was indeed deep enough to come over the horse's head, when ordinarily the depth was only some two feet. It was evident that the mass of water from the cloudburst had set up strong currents that had gouged out the bottom of the ford until it was six or eight feet deep.

A feeling that was akin to awe had settled upon the group at this warrant of the warning the clergyman had received from the stranger. Upon all of them, that is, except the old grandfather, who very matter-of-factly said, "Preacher, that were your good angel what warned ye."

In conclusion I can only say to you what Mr. Trent said to me, "There are the facts; draw your own conclusions."

Treasure

My neighbor from across the road, Linus Green,
came over this morning at my invitation to
help me use some of the grapes with which the
vines are loaded. We picked and ate awhile, and
then he asked me:

"Didn' I see Preacher Trent go in your house
yestiddy?"

"Yes," I said. "He stayed and had supper with me,
and I want to tell you a story he told me."

I barely got into the story when he stopped me,
saying:

"Yes, I've heerd that. The old gentleman h'it happened to told me about h'it himself, an' he wan't
no foolish man. I declare though, I don't know what
to make of h'it, do you?"

I confessed I did not. We ate a few more grapes
and Linus said:

"Thinkin' about preachers, I just thought about another one we used to have here about twenty years ago. He was from up North somewhere, didn' stay long though, had only been here a year or so, when in the middle of a awful hard winter he taken sick an' died out. His woman was away on a visit to her people in the North, so a letter was wrote to fine out what she wanted us to do. There wasn't no embalmers aroun' here in them days, but that wan't no problem 'cause the body were put in a shed an' h'it were way below freezin'.

"In time a answer come, an' the widder said in h'it to git a wagon an' team an' have the corpse drove down to Charleston, embalmed there, an' put on a steamboat to New York, an' she would make arrangements from there.

"A feller I knowed with a wagon an' team agreed to do the job, so the wagon was loaded with the corpse, the feller's woman packed his ration box, put in some quilts, an' that long slow trip started.

"Atter some days that driver was gettin' near Charleston, when he come to a crossroads an' was uncertain which way to go. Seein' some darkies workin' in a patch o' woods, he ask them, an' also was there a good campin' place near-by where he

could spend the night, as h'it were a'gettin' clost to
dark. They tole him how to go, an' atter awhile he
come to a good place to camp, unhitched, made him
a farr, fixed his supper an' eat h'it. Then he sat by
the farr havin' a smoke an' restin' up.

"But his rest was soon broke up, for here come
them same darkies had showed him on his way.
There was ten of 'em, an' they was all armed with
axes an' billhooks. One of 'em, a great ole big blue-
black, said to him:

" 'Now Cap'n, we all don't want no trouble, an'
there ain't goin' to be none, if'n you don't mek h'it.
We is po' folks, jus' ain't got nothin' a'tall. We knows
you is rich, an' that gre't long box on yo' wagon is
filled with treasure, gol' an' silver an' sich-like, an'
we aims to git us some of h'it.'

" 'All right Boys,' the ole feller said. 'I ain't got
ary bit of use fur what's in that box. H'it ain't makin'
me feel good havin' h'it on my wagon, so you'uns
jus' go right ahead, open her up, an holp yor-selfs.'

"Then two of them darkies jumped up on the
wheel hubs an' begin pryin' the box led off with
their axes, whilst the others all crowded round, their
eyes shinin' in the moonlight with hope an' greed.

"The led was soon pried up, an' there lay the

body of that ole preacher, dressed in his cassock an' long white surplice!

"To the end of his days that ole feller drove the wagon said never before in life did darkies run as fur an' as fast as them darkies done."

Fecundity

I was sitting at the post office this morning looking over the headlines in the paper. I had a comfortable after-breakfast feeling, my pipe was drawing nicely, a warm sun shining, a cool breeze blowing, and all was well with the world. I was about to leave and go get to work when Charl Turner came riding up on his old mare. We exchanged the usual civilities, and I asked him whether they had many summer folks staying at their house.

About half a mile above Charl Turner's house there is a lovely little waterfall, where a small creek tumbles off a seventy-five-foot cliff. This spot is famed in our region for its beauty, its fishing, and as a swimming hole for the neighborhood boys. Charl's house is a huge one, and his wife, Miss Lucy, being a famous mistress of the culinary arts, makes a practice of "keeping" summer guests.

Charl said to me, "We've just got two ladies stayin' with us now, but I reckon six or eight more folks will come in Saturday night. One of them ladies that's with us now has been here a number of times before, an' she feels like she knows all about us mountain folks. The other one is a stranger, hasn't never been here before. That knowin' one is havin' her a big time takin' t'other one aroun', showin' her the sights, an' explainin' to her about us mountain folks.

"Yestiddy mornin' they started walkin' up to the falls. They was passin' Will Butler's house, an' Will overheerd the knowin' one sayin' to that other one, 'An' My Dear, the mountain people have so many childern; now look at that little house yander,' pointing to Will's. 'I wouldn't be surprised if them people have six or seven childern.'

"So soon as they got around the bend in the path, Will lit out all over that neighborhood, a'borrowin' young-uns. He got all sizes, from growed down to one jus' a few months old. When them old ladies come back down from the falls, Will, an' his woman a'holdin' that least un, was a'settin' on the porch with twenty-nine young-uns aroun' 'em. That knowin' lady nudged 'tother one, an' spoke up to Will:

" 'Good mornin' Sir, it's a fine day.'

" 'Yes Mom,' says Will. 'Sho is.'

" 'Are these all your childern Sir?' she ask him.

" 'Oh no Mom,' says Will, 'just a part of 'em. Sally is married an' livin' in Bristol, Johnny is workin' over in Kingsport, an' I disremember whether they's three or four of the boys went to Detroit.'

"Will says you never saw the beat of the way them ladies' eyes bugged out."

A Forethoughted Man

On the way home yesterday after hearing Charl Turner's story about all those children of Will Butler's, I couldn't resist the temptation of stopping at Charl's house in the hope that the two ladies would be there. Sure enough, they were sitting on the porch talking to Mrs. Turner, who introduced me to them. I did a little "fishing," commenting upon young-uns, etc. They rose to the bait, and I heard the story all over again. I had a difficult time trying to keep my face straight.

It developed that the ladies were about to go to the store for something, and feeling a bit guilty, I drove them down in my car. I joined the group sitting on the store porch while the ladies went inside to make their purchases. Presently a boy from off the mountain came to the store with a croker sack full of "yarbs" on his shoulder. One of the men, Arlee Thompson, spoke up and said:

"Seein' that boy totin' that sack reminds me. One day last week I went to the river, see could I catch me a mess o' fish. On my way I met Monroe Brown. He was totin' two sacks. He eased 'em down, an' we sit on a rock an' talked a spell.

"Presently, pokin' one o' them sacks with the end of my fish pole, I ask him, 'What you got in that sack, Monroe?'

" 'Snake-bite medicine,' says he.

" 'What's in t'other one?' I ask him.

" 'Snakes,' he says."

I Hear Tell of Uncle Old

Our mountain people have a deeply religious background, very slightly changed from old times, and it is rather on the grim, fundamentalist order, particularly in the remote parts of the back country. For example, I once heard of a little boy walking home from church with his father. They passed a barn with a small window, out of which was thrust an unusually long head of a mule. The little boy looked at the mule and said:

"Papa, that mule must have religion."

"Why do you say that, Son?" the father asked.

"Because he's so long-faced," the boy answered.

More evidence, such lives must have some "salt" as a necessary counterpart. In every community there are a few rare souls with a natural flair for furnishing the "salt." I must tell you about such a "salty" man who lives in our community.

One day at the "Jot-'Em-Down Club" I heard a man talking about Uncle Oldham Flagg, who lived over in Cove Valley a few miles away. The man asked whether I knew him. I confessed I did not.

"Well, you orter," he said. "There ain't nothin' else like him in these parts. He's a little bitty man, not much mor'n five foot tall, got a great old big mustache, sparklin' eyes, an' he's way up in eighty. He's as full of pranks an' shines as a boy in school. He's all'us a'playin' tricks on folks, an' he can take it as good as he can hand it out.

"To show you what I mean, I stopped at Vail's store in Harmony Sat'day evenin' to git somepin' the woman wanted. Toreckly Uncle Old come in an' set with some of us boys, sort of laughin' to hisself. Presen'ly he says, 'Boys, I like to have got shot las' night. I'm lucky to be here!' O'course one o' the fellers spoke up an' ask him how come. He says:

"'You-uns know that feller Short Tom, lives up in the holler back o' me. His cows have been in my corn over an' over. I kep' a'talkin' to Tom about h'it, an' he'd apologize an' make all kine o' promises, but h'it didn' do no good much. So las' night I 'lowed I'd kinely git even with him.

"'I went to the barn, got me a cowbell, stropped

h'it round my neck good, clim' the fence, an' went over in Tom's corn patch. I went up clost to the house, so's to be sure he'd hear me, a'movin' slow an' a'jerkin' that bell, like a pickin' cow would.

" 'He heerd me all right, for t'want no time afore he pops outa the house, a'shoutin' an' a'yellin', "Git, git outa my corn, you ornery cow brute." I taken on like a cow would, lopin' here an' there, Tom a'chasin' me, me a'janglin' that bell, an' Tom jus' a'cussin'. O'course I kep' in that corn patch.

" 'By an' by h'it seem like he give out. Guess he was a'gittin' tard. I was kinely tard m'self. Anyhow he run in the house, a'slammin' the door, but Boys, t'want no time afore I seen him bust out that door agin, an' in the light a'shinin' out the door, I seen he had a shotgun. Then Boys, I raley took out, a'headin' for home hard as I could go. I wan't playin' cow no more. Tom lets one fly at me, an' I heerd shot a'rattlin' all in the corn leaves aroun' me.

" 'Whilst I was a'runnin', I were tryin' my durndest to shuck off that cussed cowbell, but t'want no use. I jus' couldn't git h'it aloose, an' the strop were too short to slip h'it over my head. Ever now an' then Tom would stop an' reload, an' then, kerplow, an' shot would spatter roun' me like hail balls.

" 'Finally, I come to that rail fence, clim' h'it, an' the chase was over. I reckon all that saved me was that Tom's gun was jus' a old single-shot affair, an' he had to keep a'stoppin' to reload.' "

My! My! What a "salt mine" Uncle Old must be! I'll have to go see that man first chance I get.

The Hastily Departing Guests

Every time I read the county newspaper I am struck afresh, when looking over the obituaries, at the advanced age at which most of the deaths occur. There must be a reason for this, and I think I have found it. The healthy climate plays its part, to be sure, but there is something else. Old people around here don't give up; they keep active. There are many light jobs they can do, split kindling, pick berries, potter in the garden, feed the chickens, etc. I went up the creek yesterday afternoon to see Lum Sowers. He is ninety-two years old and has the face of a man thirty years younger. I found the old fellow out in the cow barn pulling down hay for his cow. After completing the task, he led the way to the house, and we set our chairs out on the grass in the afternoon sunshine. He said to me:

"Preacher was here just now, left a little bit before you come. Me an' him was a'talkin' about the mean crazy goin's-on in the world today. He ast me what do I think h'it will all come to, an' how are we goin' to come out of h'it. I tole him all I can see is, when the golden sunset outshines the golden dollar, an' the golden rule outshines both of 'em, we'll come out of h'it." He went on to say:

"Speakin' about preachers leads to thinkin' about missionaries an' sich-like an calls to my mine somethin' that happened over on Laurel Cove a long time ago, when I were a young feller.

"You know most folks in these parts are Bab-dis, but the Mormons keep a'sendin' missionaries through here, an' in old days they come more often than they do now. H'it never done 'em no good though, an' folks kinely resented their comin' an' tryin' to change their religion. Them missionaries was mostly young fellers, travelin' in pairs.

"One night about supper time, two of 'em come to the house of a old feller, lived all alone over on Laurel Cove, an' wanted to stay all night. He was a goodhearted ole feller, an' not knowin' them two was Mormons, he made 'em welcome. The ole man cooked up some supper, an' then they all sat aroun' talkin', an' h'it come out that them two was Mormons.

"Now that ole man was a turble Bab-dis an' didn' want to keep no Mormons. Bein' goodhearted, he didn' want to push 'em out, but he sho' aimed to git shet of 'em, so he done some schemin'.

"Like a lot o' ole fellers, he had made him a casket agin the day 'twould be needed, an' h'it were kep' beneath his high ole corded bed. Lookin' at that casket, an idea come to him, so he says to 'em:

" 'Fellers, I got trouble, an' I need holp.'

"One of 'em says, 'Our mission in life is to holp folks. What can we do for you?'

"The ole man says: 'Well Boys, I'll tell ye. I got an awful mean neighbor in that next house, always a'fussin' an' a'racketin' 'bout nothin'. He come down here this afternoon jus' a'carryin' on, said my sheep was in his orchard. He kep' on, an' kep' on, an' I finely los' my temper an' hit him on the head with a stake. I was so mad, I hit harder than I aimed to, an' he's dead. I got him in that casket under that bed. He's too heavy for me to carry out an' bury without no holp, an' I want you fellers to holp dig the grave, carry him up back o' the barn, an' bury him. Now you-uns jus' wait while I step to the shed an' git a spade an' a mattick, an' we'll dig the grave fust. Atter h'its ready, we'll carry him out an' bury him.'

"Then that ole man went out the back door an' peeped in the winder. He got to that winder jus' in time to see them young fellers a'flyin' out the front door like the Devil was atter 'em!"

Point of View

Man is ever interested in the contemplation and study of relics from past generations. This interest is spread among people from scientists to housewives. In our modern times, in most localities, few antiques are to be found outside museums. I am by no means immune to the attraction of such things myself and have spent many happy hours visiting collections in scattered parts of the country from the deep South to New England. It is still possible to find in and around Dutch Cross a few of the old-time articles of everyday use, such things as corded beds, froes, broadaxes, pots and kettles of iron, brass and copper, ancient pieces of furniture made of choice wood, rifles, tools, etc. Then too, there are a few of the old-time log houses. These were made of hand-hewn timbers, cleverly notched and dovetailed at the corners, and covered with rived boards.

Once, I even found one that had a rived picket fence around it. To me, these old cabins are well-nigh perfect artistically. I have often wondered whether their builders proceeded from knowledge, instinct, or a combination of both.

I went out to look at such an old cabin this morning, one that I have been told can be bought, but it was in such bad condition I passed it by. I have restored two or three such old cabins and had a lot of pleasure doing it. The logs in one of them were nearly two hundred years old, and in surprisingly good condition.

Last summer I bought one of these ancient cabins, numbered the logs, had them taken down and hauled several miles from their site, and restored the cabin on a lot in Dutch Cross for a Florida lady. This undertaking was watched and interestedly kept up with daily by a number of the local men.

One day, Monroe Brown, though rather puny, climbed up the hill to where we were working and made a close examination all around. He finished his investigation and sat down, whereupon I asked him what he thought of it.

"Hell's fire," he said, "you could'a built a rale house for what this is goin' to cost."

He let that soak in, and then he asked me:

"What you goin' to do with them walls on the inside?"

"Oh," said I, "after we get the cracks chinked, I'm going to leave them just like they are; I think they are beautiful."

"By Grabs, I wouldn't," was his rejoinder. "If h'it was me, I'd panel h'it, cover up them damn logs, so I couldn't see 'em."

I scarcely need tell you, Monroe was born and raised in a log house!

War & Peace

I had to go to Boone, our county seat, this morning to have some work done on my car. As the work would take a good part of the morning, I dropped in for a visit with Ben Turner, Charl's son, and a chip off the old block. As we sat out on the porch talking, a queer old man walked by whom I had often seen around the town. He was a dirty dun brown from the crown of his ancient hat to the toes of his worn brogans. His attire had the look of being an integral part of him, grown to his body. He wore a short beard, brown too, but patched here and there with a dirty gray. What one could see of his face showed a tracery of wrinkles, etched in dark lines, which could only be ingrained dirt. I asked Ben who that was, and he said:

"That's old man Ball. I thought everyone knew

him. He lives a little way up the mountain back of the town in a patchwork cabin made out of odds and ends. He lives all alone and makes a bare living doing odd jobs in the village. Some folks say he never takes off his clothes except to change to something warmer when Winter comes, and to something cooler when Spring comes.

"He has a next-door neighbor, Linville Pines. He's a colored man, has a family, is a good worker and is well thought of in the town. The two men are always falling out, don't get on together at all well, continually racketing about some little thing, though it seems like they made it up now. I'll tell you how come 'em to make peace.

"One morning last Spring Linville came out his door to go to his work. It was a Monday. The previous Saturday he had planted his garden. He turned his head to give one more look of pride at the pretty little garden he had made behind his cottage. Rage flew over him. Ball's chickens were all over that garden, busy as could be scratching up seeds. Linville flew over to old Ball's shack, and they lost no time getting into it. They abused one another scandalously. Finally Linville walked off, shouting all kinds of threats about lawing Ball. The court house was right on his route, so in he popped and swore out a warrant for him. A deputy served the warrant and brought old Ball in. Court was in session, and the old man was turned loose in his own recognizance, to come back next morning for trial.

"When morning came Ball failed to show up, so a deputy had to be sent out to bring him in.

"The court docket was crowded, and the case being so trifling, the two men were taken into the magistrate's chamber to see couldn't they fix it without having to go to trial. But Lord! Those two got into a hot cuss fight, and it would soon have been a fist fight, 'cept the magistrate lost patience and shouted 'Lock 'em both up.' So they were taken downstairs to the jail and pushed into adjoining cells. Here the argument went on and on, until both were give out. Then Ball got to worrying over being in jail and began to shout, 'I want out o' here.' Presently his shouting turned to prayer:

" 'Oh Lord, I want out o' here. Holp me get out Lord. Damn it Lord cain't you hear me? I tell you I want out.' Linville soon joined him, and they prayed at the top of their voices to the Lord to let them out. Then old Ball started a hymn in his old cracked voice, Linville joining in with his deep bass.

Then they prayed some more, and sang two more hymns.

"Now something really happened. Reaching through the bars of their cells, they took each other by the hand in the firm clasp of fellowship. Just then the jailer came down the corridor and opened their cell doors, and the two men walked out arm in arm. If they have had a racket since, I haven't heard of it, but I'm waiting."

I wonder, when the magistrate had the two men jailed, was that a "judgment of Solomon," or merely happenstance?

Hot Stuff

There is a rocky gorge down below Sloan Hammond's, through which the Watauga River flows into Tennessee. There are many spots along it of interest and excitement to a landscape painter. The hills down there are incredibly steep. I know of one so steep the hay is cut with a "mowin' size," and when it is cured, rolled down the hillside to the foot and there put up into stacks. I often sketch along that gorge.

One morning last week, after an early start, having finished my painting about mid-morning, I stopped at "Uncle Sloan's" for a visit. When I went in, the old gentleman was, as usual, sitting alongside the stove, reading his Bible-study books. He made me warmly welcome, gave me a chair, and before very long Miss Lizzie came into the room insisting that I must stay and "eat dinner." I didn't need much persuading, as a bachelor or widower seldom does when he is invited to eat.

In due time Miss Lizzie called us to the "ration board," and, as usual, she had a fine meal set out. As we started on the dinner she said to me, "Try some of this pepper sauce on your cabbages, if you like 'em hot." "Uncle Sloan" warned me that the sauce was hot indeed, being homemade from little red peppers out of their garden. Of course those hot peppers reminded him of a story, which he promised to tell me after dinner.

Dinner over, "Uncle Sloan" and I retired to the stoveside in the bedroom, and after we had our pipes going, he related his promised story to me.

"In my young days there used to be a man lived way back up on Elk. When he was just a boy, his family moved out to Texas, stayed there a little while, an' then went to Mexico, an' stayed there twenty years or more. Then the family broke up, got scattered, some of 'em died out, an' one thing an' another, an' that boy, now a man o'course, decided he wanted to come back to where he was raised at. Hodge, I think was his name. He bought him a little place back close to the old home place, an' settled down, him by now havin' a woman an' several childern.

"One night he went to a big revival meetin', an' kep' a'goin', didn' miss a meetin'. He sho' got religion, an' the next thing he knowed h'it seemed like he 'got the call,' so he become a preacher. O'course he done a little farmin' too, an' he got on pretty good. He was plumb happy 'cept for one thing . . . his rations didn' taste good, seemed watery, didn' have no flavor much. You see, he had lived all them years out in Mexico, where the people season up everythin' they eat with hot peppers an' I don't know what all. Well, Hodge wrote him a letter to some frien's back in Mexico an' got them to send him seeds of all kinds of hot peppers, an' sich like. Whenever they come, he planted them seeds in his garden, an' when them peppers was growed good, his woman would crush 'em an' put 'em with vinegar, maybe bile 'em some, an' can the sauce. That done h'it! His rations tasted good agin, an' he was as happy as a coon in a holler log.

"One day he was called to court in Boone to witness in a big murder trial. He put the saddle on his horse an' was about to start out when h'it come to him that trial might last several days, meanin' he would have to stay over there in the hotel. So, to be prepared, he called his old woman an' had her to fix him a bottle o' that hot sauce, poked h'it in his saddle bags, an' set out.

"Well, sure enough, the court docket was crowded an' the trial drawed out, an' he had to stay at the old Critcher Hotel. One day he was sittin' in the dinin' room, eatin' his dinner, his little bottle o' hot sauce alongside him, when a travelin' man, a saleman, come in an' set down beside him, orderin' his dinner. When the waiter brought h'it, set h'it down, the saleman tasted h'it, looked up an' saw that bottle alongside Hodge. He ask the waiter to pass him over that bottle of pepper sauce. The waiter said he couldn't do that because h'it was private, belonged to that gentleman over there. Hodge spoke right up an' tole the saleman he was welcome to help hisself. So the saleman took h'it an' doused h'it all over his beans an' cabbage, an' stuff. Then he took him a big bite, chewed h'it a little, an' then started suckin' in wind an' pantin' like a dog in fly time. He took him a big drink o' water, sloshed buttermilk aroun' in his mouth, sucked some more wind, looked over at Hodge an' ask him what was his occupation. Hodge tole him he was a preacher. The saleman ask him did he preach Hell an' Damnation. Hodge says, 'I shore do.' 'Well,' says the saleman, 'you are the first preacher I ever knowed that carried samples.' "

The Purple Sow

In our rural life fences are of paramount importance. They, and their condition, have much to
do with how one gets on with the family on the
adjoining place.

Alas! They are unendingly needing attention.
Horses and cows do their scratching on topmost
rails and posts, sheep and hogs on the lower levels.
People climb over them, fox hunters don't hesitate
to use the rails for firewood, when the hounds are
chasing foxes over the mountains at night, and
heavy rains often wash deep gullies under them.
Repairing them presents no prospect of immediate
cash returns, as do other jobs like taking a load of
cabbage, beans or tobacco to market. It calls for a
strong character and determination to go fix that
North fence as soon as a man knows it needs work

done on it. If everyone kept up fine fences, there wouldn't be much to fuss about, and many of the stories in this book would not be here.

Several miles down Watauga River two men live on adjoining farms. They are both successful, and the two families are on good neighborly terms. Last year one of the men, Ed Mills, had a big sow of a most peculiar purple color. Much of the time this sow was out of the pen and roaming the farm at will. Fences, if not too stout, didn't mean anything to her, and she was often on the adjoining farm, rooting and tearing up the ground and making a general nuisance of herself.

Jeff Bord, the neighbor, would often come over for a visit, and would complain to Ed in a nice way about the sow. Ed would apologize and make all kinds of promises to keep her at home. However, the nuisance did not abate. Finally Jeff lost his temper one day and told Ed the next time that purple sow came over on him, he would set the dogs on her, get his hog rifle, kill her, and send word to Ed to come get her and butcher her. Then Jeff left in a huff.

Ed sat on the porch thinking matters over. He wasn't exactly angry, the men were too good friends for that, but it seemed clear something would have to be done.

Ed's old white mare was grazing in front of the house. As he sat idly watching her, she switched off on another tack, and Ed saw some kind of a purplish mark on her rump. He walked out to her for a closer look and found the purplish mark was a letter M. All of a sudden it struck him that the color of that letter M was almost identically the color of his purple sow. It occurred to him that the "young-uns" had probably been playing a wild west game of some kind, which had called for the branding of the mare. He started an inquiry and found that this was indeed so, and that the color the boys had used was pokeberry juice.

Ed went back to the porch and sat there quite a while, trying to nail down some sort of an elusive idea that was floating around in the back of his head. All of a sudden it hit him in a flash.

He called the two oldest boys and told them to take their .22 rifle and go over on Jeff's place and make out like they were hunting birds, but to hem up that white sow of Jeff's and drive her over some-how to Ed's barn shed. Ed then got some more of the young-uns to help him, each one with a bucket, and they went down along the creek bank back of the house, where pokeberries grew in profusion. In a short time they were back at the barn, their buckets full of berries. Ed got one of his wife's wash-tubs from the house, poured pokeberries in it, and mashed them, making the strongest tincture he could.

It wasn't long until the two biggest boys came back, driving Jeff's white sow. They got her in the barn shed, put a rope on her so she had to stand, then proceeded to cover her with pokeberry juice, using an old paint brush. When they finished she looked like twin sister to Ed's purple sow. Then they turned her loose, and she high-tailed for home.

When she got home Jeff was out in the barn lot repairing a broken sled. Out of the tail of his eye he saw something moving, looked up, and there was that danged old "purple" sow of Ed Mills' again. He ran in the house, got his rifle, and out again. Taking careful aim, he pulled the trigger, and the "purple" sow dropped in her death throes.

That was satisfaction number one. Now for satisfaction number two. He saddled his horse, and away he went to Ed Mills' house.

Of course Ed had made sure that the genuine

purple sow was securely penned, and he was sitting on the porch smoking his pipe and awaiting a visitor when Jeff rode up. Jeff said, "Ed, I'm sorry, but I want to tell you I'm a man of my word. I shot that old purple sow of yours a little bit ago over on my place, an' you better come an' git her out o' my way. The meat orter be saved."

Ed rose from his chair, knocked out his pipe and said, "Jeff, I don't know which one of us is crazy. Come with me. I want to show you somethin'." Ed took Jeff to the back of the barn where his hog pen was, and there, dozing in the sun, lay the old purple sow!

That Jeff must be an amiable man with a keen sense of humor, for it is told that the next night the two families supped together on fresh pork tenderloin!

A Visit to Uncle Old

One afternoon several years ago I was sitting out in the yard with a friend, Bob Elliot, a fellow artist who had come to spend a few days with me. Bob is a New York City man who had never before been in our Southern mountains. The country, the people, everything was new to him and he was tremendously interested in observing it all.

We were about to start out on a drive when a car drove into the yard. The driver turned out to be a good friend, Tom Peters. Tom lives in Charlotte but has a summer place in Linville. He said that he was on his way back to Linville, but seeing us, had stopped for a pop call. We relaxed in our chairs, a cold drink in one hand, a smoke in the other, and settled down for some good man-talk.

The cross-country bus lines had just started running through our section of the mountains. There was no competition yet, the Greyhound being the only line we saw. Bob had come down from New York on the bus and told us he had greatly enjoyed the trip, despite its being long and somewhat tedious. He went on to tell us of an incident that had happened a few miles before the bus got to Boone. An ancient man had come out of a house and had flagged the bus. The driver stopped, anticipating another passenger, but the old man made no move to get on. Instead, he stood there and said to the driver:

"Son, I cain't go with ye. I jus' stopped ye to tell ye, she's a dandy, an' I want to speak fur a pup out'a the first litter she has."

We laughed and Tom asked Bob:

"Was he a little man, not much over five feet, a big walrus mustache, and carrying a long staff?"

"Yes," said Bob, "that's the man. Is it possible you know him?"

Tom chuckled and said, "I sure do know him. That couldn't have been anyone other than Uncle Oldham Flagg on John's Gap. He's just full of pranks like that. Let me tell you how I first met him.

"About two years ago I was driving past his house on my way to do some fishing. He came hobbling out of the house, leaning on that long staff, and stopped me.

" 'Say,' he says, 'air ye in a big hurry, Son?'

"I was hesitating how to answer him when he went on:

" 'I got a dog I set a heap o' store by. A while ago two fellers walked down the road in the direction you jus' come from, an' my dog follered them. I'm afeard them fellers will steal him, an' I'd like to git you to turn aroun' an' ride me down a piece, see can we find him. I cain't call him, 'cause I cain't remember his name, an' I cain't whistle for him 'cause my teeth are s'bad!' "

As we say around here, "that done it," and I proposed that we drive over and see Uncle Old. Tom, being a bachelor, and living alone, agreed to spend the night with us, so we piled in the car and set out, with only about half an hour's drive ahead of us.

We found the old gentleman sitting on his porch with four hound dogs. He made us a warm welcome, called his wife, and had her bring us a pitcher of cold buttermilk. She set it down and said:

"I sure am glad you men come. Maybe you can

calm him down some. He's all excited today."

I enquired the cause of the excitement and he said:

"Son, I got me a new autymobile yestiddy."

I congratulated him and asked what make it was. He replied:

"Why, urra, urra, urra, damn if I can remember, but she's a dandy."

Uncle Old needed no questioning or drawing out. The words just tumbled out of his mouth. First off he positively bragged that he was ninety-two years old. I have often noticed that a young man is apt to add on a bit when telling his age, a middle-aged man is inclined to take off a little, while from about seventy upward a man will proudly reveal to you the number of his years, maybe adding on a bit, to be certain that you are properly impressed with his triumph over the passing of the years.

At the time the Second World War was going on, and things were not going well for our side. Uncle Old said:

"This war is turble. I got three gran'sons in h'it, but I reckon wars are all bad. I was in the Yankee war. I went to the Confederate camp near here an' tried to jine up, but they wouldn't have me, bein's

I were only fifteen years old. The officer said I was
too little an' too young. People here was pretty well
divided up in their feelin's an' there was a Yankee
camp a little over the state line in Tennessee, so I
crossed over an' ast to jine them. The Yankee officer
said, just like the Confederate, that I were too little
an' too young. I pinted to a fat lazy-lookin' one o' his
men an' said, 'If I waller that feller will you take
me?' An' the officer said he would, that soldier bein'
a right smart bigger'n me. Now I were always a
purty good wrastler, so didn' have no trouble much
wallerin' that fat feller, so the officer let me jine, an'
I fit with the Yankees till the end o' the war. Never
did git hurt. I were too small a target I reckon."

Peering out at a man walking by in the road, he
asked:

"Who's that feller? Oh, I know, h'it's that brother
o' the preacher's what's a'visitin' him. Reminds me.
One Sunday las' month my woman invited the
preacher for dinner. She had a good fine dinner
cooked up, the main dish bein' a boiled ox tongue.
But that preacher is kinely picky about his vittles,
an' wouldn't take no tongue. Said he never et nothin'
from the mouth. So I told the woman, 'Cook him
some aigs.' "

It was remarkable how the old man's mind flashed from one thing to another. He went on and on like a professional entertainer, while we, his audience, sat in rapt enjoyment. Next, he came out with this:

"I were at a gatherin' up at Hill's Mills one day las' week. You know most o' them people are Dimocrats, me bein' a Republican. A feller I knowed come up to me, said, 'How'ya, Uncle Old, how'ya feelin'?' I looked aroun' at all them Dimocrats an' answered him, 'Son, I feel jus' like a grain o' rice in a barrel o' things rats drapped.'

With hardly a pause the scene switched over the state line:

"Me an' my driver was over in Tennessee yestiddy tryin' out my new autymobile, when we come to a leetle old-timey log house with a mud-an'-stick chimley. I hadn't saw a mud-an'-stick chimley for years, so I had my driver to stop, an' I got out to take a clost look at h'it. A feller come out o' the house, an' I tole him I didn't want nothin', was jus' admirin' his mud-an'-stick chimley, an' ast him did h'it draw good. He said, 'H'it shore do. You are the fifth durn fool h'it has drawed today.'"

When we swallowed that one he jumped to another.

"Folks aroun' here need stirrin' up now an' then. I give a number o' folks in the settlement some exercise this mornin'. Had to go up on the mounting this mornin' to salt my cattle. When I come back someone at the store ast me how was Aunt Julie, she a'livin' up that way; an' her havin' been kinely puny-like, I tole 'em, 'She's a'dyin'. The word went aroun' fast, an' in a little bit folks were a'streamin' up that rough road to Aunt Julie's, some of 'em a'carryin' vittles an' sich. Some o' them folks was awful mad at me, 'cause Aunt Julie was out in the yard a'dyin' yarns fur her weavin'.'"

In the face of warm solicitations to "stay all night," we made our departure, laughing all the way home. I feel sure that on many an occasion Uncle Old has dulled the sharp edge of sorrow and anxiety among the people around him.

St. Paul & Farmer Paul

I was sitting on the porch after dinner today having a smoke when "King Hal" came walking by. I hailed him and asked him to come up and sit a spell with me, and I would drive him home when he had to leave.

Across the road there is a very fine field of corn belonging to my neighbor, Harry Turner, one of Charl's boys. "King Hal" duly admired it and then said to me:

"Lookin' at that corn puts me in mine o' somethin' funny happened up our way one time.

"You remember a leetle white church house at the head o' that long holler below me? The preacher lives on that leetle farm on the upper side o' h'it. He ain't a very good farmer an' don't do no good at h'it much, jus' don't know how to manage, jus' barely feeds his family with what he makes off h'it an' what little he gits from the church. The po' feller is always givin' out o' somethin' or other an' has to scheme an' borrow to git by.

"Las' summer he was a'havin' a big revival meetin' at his church an' in the time o' h'it he plum give out o' corn. His woman didn't have no meal to make bread. He's got a neighbor lives up back o' him, man named Paul, a goodhearted accommodatin' kind o' feller; an' that preacher is always a'callin' on him for this or that. Well, he couldn't think o' nothin' else, so he called one o' his boys an' tole him to go up to Paul's an' see could he borrow a leetle corn to tide 'em over. The boy got gone an' in a leetle while the meetin' got started. The prayin' an' singin' part was over, an' the preacher was up in the pulpit under a full head o' steam, a'layin' h'it into the sinners for all he was worth, when that boy come back from Paul's. H'it were a warm summer night, an' the church house winders was all open. The pulpit is right alongside one o' the winders, an' the preacher was in high gear. Jus' as that boy got alongside o' that winder by the pulpit, that ole preacher hollered out rale loud in the course o' his preachin', 'An', what did Paul say?' That boy 'lowed his pap were a'askin' him how he made out gittin' corn from Paul, so he stuck his head in the winder an' hollered at his pap, 'Paul says you don't git no more till ye pay for what you done got already.' "

The story done, the "King" said he must get on home, so we got in the car and I drove him up the mountain. When we got to his house his wife was just removing from the fireplace a "Dutch oven" of cornbread she had baked for supper. I was urged to stay for the meal but couldn't as I had callers coming, so she insisted upon breaking off a large piece of that pone of bread for me to take home. I had it for supper that night, it was wonderful, and all the time I was eating it I thought of the poor preacher whose "wife had no meal to make bread."

The Keen Salesman

One lazy afternoon recently I was sitting on the porch at Morse's store drinking a coke and talking with the proprietor, Henry Morse. It was an ideal day for "loafering" and lazily passing the time, and we were making the best of it. But the traveling salesmen had been out in full force, brought out no doubt by the fine weather. At any rate, they kept coming, one after another, until finally things got quiet again, when Henry said to me, "I used to follow that work myself, and knowin' what they are up against, I try to treat 'em nice, but sometimes it gets awful old.

"I remember one time back in Dad's days, when he was runnin' the store, a fresh kind of salesman come in. He was awful biggity, just seemed to rub folks the wrong way whatever he said. He was a

new one, none of us had ever seen him before, and we didn't know anythin' about the firm he was representin'. Dad kept a'tellin' him we didn't need any more goods, but he just kept a'talkin', but finally saw it was no use, so he give up and started out the door.

"There was a bunch loaferin' around who had been listenin' to what was going on, an' figurin' to have some fun, one of 'em said to that salesman, 'Say Mister, I'll tell you where maybe you could get a good order. Have you tried the Hall Grocery Co. up on Beech Mountain? It's a new store, just startin', an' you might do good with 'em.'

"The salesman was keen for business an' wanted to know all about it, so they gave him exact directions how to get there, an' off that man flew.

"He had a lot of trouble findin' the place, twisted an' turned, got lost a time or two, but finally found Old Man Hall's house. The old feller didn't even have a store buildin', just used one room of his house where he kept a few things like flour, an' sugar, an' salt, maybe a little canned stuff.

"The salesman went up to the door an' knocked, the old man come to the door, an' the salesman said he had been told Mr. Hall was openin' a new store, an' if so, he would like to sell him some goods. Old Man Hall said he reckoned not, that he had about all he needed.

"Meantime the salesman had been lookin' all around, an' not seein' a store anywhere asked, 'Where do you do your business, Mr. Hall?'

" 'Why,' the old man said, 'the woman does hers under that big old sycamore up yander, but I do mine over in them laurel bushes.' "

Scholarship

When Henry Morse finished telling me the fore-going story, customers came and he had to go attend to them. I was finishing my coke and trying to drum up enough energy to start home when, the last customer attended to, Henry came back out and said, "I've got another old-time story about orderin' goods you might like to hear.

"When Dad was runnin' the store Charl Turner was in partners with him for a while, an' Charl's old daddy was too. Back in those days there weren't no travelin' salesmen much, roads were bad, there were no automobiles in these parts, an' what salesmen did come would come to Boone on the railroad, or else Spruce Pine, then hire a horse an' buggy an' drive over here. We didn't have any telephones either in those days, so when a store needed goods a letter would be sent to the wholesale house in Johnson City, or maybe Bristol.

"One mornin' Uncle Henry, that was Charl's daddy, was writin' out an order to mail in, us others helpin' suggestin' this an' that, when customers started comin' to trade, an' what with one thing an' another the order list had to be laid aside till late in the evenin'.

"Things havin' quieted down by then we started goin' over the list to be sure everythin' was on it that ought to be. But we were havin' a time. Here an' there we could make out a word, but Uncle Henry's writin' was so bad that most of it was just a mystery to us. Uncle Henry was right there too, but that didn't help us any as he couldn't read his own writin' any better than the rest of us. Finally, as we weren't gettin' anywhere, Uncle Henry says, 'Well Boys, let's just send her in. Them fellers over there are better scholars than we are. Maybe they can read it.'

"An' by Gosh, they did. Everything we needed came!"

Painting & Neighboring

There was a heavy frost last night. Autumn is here. I got up early this morning and set out for John's Gap to do some sketching.

Our Blue Ridge Mountains are covered with a large variety of deciduous trees and when the timber is "ripe" present a magnificent show. This morning the colors were splendid. The sky was a deep blue, which in contrast had the effect of intensifying the warm colors of the foliage. A chill morning wind came down off the mountains, bringing the fine smells of woodsmoke, frying ham, coffee and ripe timber. Every now and then I would stop, weighing the possibilities on canvas of the subject before me.

On one such stop a man came down the hill on a footpath, climbed the fence and gave me Good

Morning. I said to him that it had turned pretty chilly in the night. His rejoinder was, "Yup, too tool for torn, jus' right for tabbage."

Not having found anything yet to set off the desire to paint, I proceeded on up the road, soon passing Uncle Oldham Flagg's house. My attention was caught by a very professional looking sign mounted on the front lawn. To my astonishment it read, "Don't ask me to sign your note." It was quite obvious what the circumstances were that lay back of the erection of such a sign, but I resolved to make a stop on my way back and hear a first-hand account.

The John's Gap Road ascends in a series of loops. On one of the upper loops my eye was caught by a stunning scene. I set up my easel, got out my paint kit and went to work. Up here the wind was much stronger and carried the cold of the night that had lain on the mountain tops. Painting with bare hands in a chill wind is cold work, and every now and then I would lay down my brush and slap my arms against my chest to restore circulation.

Below me perhaps half a mile was a small cabin. Presently I saw a man come out the door of it and start climbing the steep hill toward me. After a stiff climb he landed on the road beside me and gave me a cheery Good Morning. Then, in an apologetic sort of way, he said, "I seen ye a'throwin' yore arms about like you was cold, an' I 'lowed I'd come up an' build ye a farr alongside your work." I had never seen the man before in my life. Perhaps a skeptic would say that was just an excuse he made to come up and satisfy his curiosity as to what I was doing, but from many years of experiencing the kindliness of the mountain people, I would strongly deny such a sour view. At any rate, I assured the man that his thought and consideration were as warming as any fire.

Finishing my sketch, I packed my things and, turning, headed down the mountain, anticipating the fun of a visit with Uncle Old on my homeward way. When I went to the door the old gentleman came out to meet me, despite the chill, and made me warmly welcome. After the customary amenities I said to him that I had come on business, that I wanted him to endorse my note for five hundred dollars. He chuckled and said:

"Son, that sign out there is sure earnin' wages. Ain't nobody ast me to sign a note for 'em since I had her put up. I jus' got tard of havin' to pay other folks' promises. Now I don't have to turn nobody down an' maybe cause hard feelin's. I'm gittin' too old to suck hind teats." He went on:

"Say, did you notice that lean, mangy-lookin' feller out thar a'paintin' my house? No, I reckon you never saw him, cause he's a'workin' on the back-side of the house; backsides is jus' about his speed. I fixed him good. At the FCX fire sale las' year I bought a big bunch o' paint at a bargain price. H'it was plum good paint, jus' the cans kinely smoked up some. Then I got three different fellers to bid on a contract to put h'it on the house, all o' h'it, every drap, so's to be sure o' havin' a good job that would last. That feller out thar named the lowest price so he got the contract.

"We let that lower end o' the garden lay out last summer. This Spring my gran'son, Bill, was a'turnin' h'it with a shovel plough an' down in that corner he turned up three cans o' paint that scoun'rel had buried in the garden to save the trouble o' puttin' h'it on the house accordin' to contract. So, h'it took me a time, but I made him come back, never give him no peace till he come, an' now he's a'paintin' an' a'grumblin'. I may be ole an' ignorant, but I'm hard to fool."

Just then a man drove a truck with three refrigerators on it into the yard, got out and stepped up on the porch, saying, "I brought them refrigerators you ordered, Mr. Flagg."

"All right Son," said the old man. "Gimme your bill, I'll make ye a check, an' then I'll tell ye where to put 'em." The man passed him a bill for some seven or eight hundred dollars. Uncle Old went in his little back room and soon reappeared with a check, which he handed over to the driver. The man thanked him, folded it and put it in his pocket. Then he said:

"Mr. Flagg, I can't help wondering how a man living way out here in the sticks like you do can have enough money to buy himself an' two girls a refrigerator apiece, all at one time."

Uncle Old said, "Son, I made a mistake on that check I give you. Hand her back, an' I'll show ye."

The man handed it back. Uncle Old took it and deliberately tore it to bits, and said:

"Now Son, you needn't to worry no more about how I git my money. Instid you can start worryin' about what you goin' to tell your boss man when you take them refrigerators back to the store."

I never saw nor expect to see another man as

chapfallen as that driver. He apologized, begged, pleaded, but all to no avail. As the man drove off Uncle Old said:

"I can git the same outfit from 'Monkey' Ward at the same price. I jus' had to learn that feller to mind his own business."

Spirits, Animal & Grain

This morning I was walking down Watauga River bank with our local game warden when we came to a big tree in front of the house of Fate McCoy. Fate is a middle-aged, red-headed man, smart, witty and has done many a job for me. His failing is an inordinate love of white corn liquor. He enjoys a small pension from his army service, and when his monthly check arrives, he loses no time in drinking it down. A local man once reproached Fate with having run through three fine farms. All he got from Fate was, "You are wrong, they run through me."

As we drew near we saw Fate and a crony of his, old man Jack Benton, sitting under the big tree on the bank, Fate holding a homemade fish pole. The game warden started giving Fate a lecture for fishing after the close of the season. Fate stopped him, gave a sly grin and said:

"You fellers sit down an' I'll show ye what kind o' fish I'm a'gittin'."

With that he took a quick look over his shoulder at the house, but his wife—whom he calls the superintendent—was not in sight. He slowly lifted the tip of his pole and drew the "fish" in to the bank. It was a quart bottle of white corn, which he hospitably extended to us! We declined, but Fate and Jack each took a dram, after which Fate carefully let the "fish" swim back into the river.

Just before supper time I met the warden, Tommy, at the store, and we had another good laugh over Fate's "fish." Tommy then told me that he had told his brother about our seeing Fate and Jack "fishing," and his brother had then told Tommy about another exploit of the same two men which took place last Saturday. As Tommy's brother, Chris, described it:

"When I come around the big bend in the river, I saw Fate and Jack leanin' on the fence watchin' two sheep in Charley Chapel's meadow. Them sheep had their heads pressed together, pushin' and buttin' like sheep do. I could see Fate an' Jack were

plumb high, an' they were laughin' their heads off.
First thing I knew them two idiots climbed over the
fence, got down on all fours, put their heads together, an' pushed an' butted jus' like them sheep
were doin'. Every now an' then they would stop an'
take another dram, then go back to pushin' an' buttin'. They didn't pay no attention to me, too drunk
to know I was there I reckon. I guess I must'a
watched 'em for near half an hour, an' I guess I
was laughin' as hard as they were."

Having made my purchase in the store, I was
about to start home when Fate himself came driving up in a wagon drawn by the biggest ox I ever
saw. He had pretty well digested his "fish," though
they had left him in a talkative mood. He said that
the "fish" quit biting before they got enough. We
twitted him about playing sheep, and he admitted:

"H'it were foolish. I ain't got as much wool on top
o' my head as a sheep has, an' my old skull is plumb
sore. Say, you'uns ain't saw nobody lookin' fur me,
have ye?"

Assuring him we had not, we questioned him as
to whom he was dodging, and why. Bit by bit the
story came out; put together the bits came to this:

"Last Tuesday I rode over to Bristol with Fred
Patrick in his pick-up. He let me off down town an'

said for me to meet him at the depot at four o'clock. I got a pint from a feller I knowed an' walked aroun' seein' the town. Ever' now an' then I'd slip in a place an' take me another dram, till 'fore I knowed h'it that bottle was empty an' I was feelin' purty good. Then I meets the law, an' the way he talked to me I didn't feel so good. Said they didn' want no North Ca'lina fellers a'gittin' drunk in their town, an' all like that. Then he said he was a'goin' to put me in the "Crossbar Hotel." That good glow I had was a'liftin' fast, an' my head workin' better, I done some quick thinkin'. Then I tole that cop I already had trouble, an' he shouldn't make me no more. He wanted to know what kine of trouble, so I tole him there was a good ole colored man had lived over by me, a neighbor, that he had died out, an' I wanted to fine his boy to tell him about his pappy a'dyin'. He ask me the boy's name an' where did he live at, so I retch in my pocket an' pulled out a paper I happened to have with that boy's name an' address on h'it, an' give h'it to the cop. That cop plumb changed, went with me, holped me fine the house, an' was plumb nice.

"I tole that colored feller about his daddy a'dyin', an' about this nice cop holpin' me fine him, the cop swellin' up in the time o' h'it an' a'lookin' plumb proud. Boys, them darkies sure carried on, sent young-uns all over to tell the other kin, an' purty soon here they come, about twenty of 'em I reckon, an' a'ridin' in four cars. That boy made me git in his car, an' we started for home, all four cars. O'course h'it were way pas' time to meet Fred at the depot.

"When we come to Harmony I tole 'em to let me out, an' I'd take the near cut across the hill afoot an' drive the cows in on my way. They wanted to drive me home in their car, but I didn't want 'em to do that.

"They couldn't hardly quit thankin' me for comin' over atter 'em, all the trouble I'd took, an' so on, even wantin' to pay me, but my likker had plumb wore off an' I knowed I better git gone without no delay.

"I heerd atterwards that when they come to the old darky's house he were a'settin' on the porch a'eatin' a baked sweet 'tater, an' them coloreds was mad as hornets. I reckon they done gone back to Bristol, but I ain't takin' no chances.

"I hear Fred is kinely mad at me too. Seems he waited at that depot for me till five-thirty."

Testing the Telephone

A man going up the mountain this morning stopped by my house and told me that I was wanted on the long distance telephone at the store. Although the call was not from a great distance, being only from Charlotte, I had a lot of difficulty in hearing, and it was harder still to make my voice heard at the other end. Before I was done I was shouting just about as loud as I can, and having to repeat over and over what I wanted to say. My caller and I finally succeeded in making ourselves understood to each other, and I joined the small group of "Jot-'Em-Down Club" members around the stove. As I sat down Lum Sowers said:

"You a'yellin' on the telephone like you jus' done puts me in mine o' when the phone first come to these parts. H'it were back before the first World's

War commenced. Folks here was rale excited, an'
all they could think about was them phones. They
was the old-timey kine, hung on the wall with a
crank you had to turn to ring 'em.

"Atter they was all in, a bunch o' us was a'settin'
roun' the store one day a'listenin' at fellers a'usin'
h'it, when Walt Wagnalls come in. He listened at
the talk awhile an' then said, 'Boys, we orter test
that phone, be sure she's a'workin' right. Let's git
Squire Billy Sparr to holp us.'

"I don't reckon you ever knowed Squire Billy
Sparr. He died out afore you come I expect. He
heired a fine farm, an' had a good livin' off h'it.
On top o' that he was a magistrate an' a notary, an'
right proud o' bein' them things too. He wan't the
kine to catch on to things rale quick an' size up a
situation right away, so somebody was always
teasin' him about somethin' or ruther.

"Well, Walt started crankin' Squire Bill's ring.
He lived across the road a leetle ways, so some of
the fellers knowed Walt was up to devilment went
over thar to listen at 'tother end. When Squire
answered, Walt said:

" 'Squire Sparr, this is the Telephone Company.
We want to test your telephone. Will you holp us?'

" 'Yes Sir,' said the Squire, 'What mus' I do?'

"Walt says, 'Stand about two feet to the right of the phone an' holler Hello, good an' loud.' Squire done that.

"Walt says, 'That's good. Now try h'it two feet to the left, an' holler a little louder.' Squire done that, this time jus' a'yellin'.

"Walt says, 'Now git you a cheer, stand up on h'it, an' holler Hello.'

So the ole feller done that. Then Walt had him to try sittin' on the floor, kneelin' on h'it, every time tellin' him to holler Hello a leetle louder. Then Walt tole him to git the stepladder an try from h'it, an' please to holler louder. H'it finally ended when Walt tole him to stand on his head on the cheer an' holler Hello. The ole feller caught on then that somebody was a'makin' fun o' him, an' he was mad as farr. That Walt, he sure was a prankin' character, but nobody never stayed mad at him long. I never heerd a harm word said 'bout him, 'cause there wasn't no malicy in what he done."

A Pioneer Sees the Sights

A friend from Charlotte and his wife, who are vacationing at Little Switzerland, drove over today to visit me. They had much to tell me of the terrific damage done over there by the summer's flood. Their visit has set me thinking about old days when I frequently spent weekends and holidays at Little Switzerland. In those days the journey there from the low country was made by railway, there being no motor roads in that section. The nearest railway station was about three miles down the mountain from the inn. At one end of the station the railway tracks emerged from a tunnel onto a small plateau on which the station stood, and at the other end the tracks disappeared into another tunnel. From the station to the inn the journey was completed by horse-drawn hack.

There was an old man living not far from the inn who was a great favorite with the guests at the inn. Billy Fields was his name, but he was known to about everybody as "Uncle Billy." He was a great teller of tales dealing with hunting, fishing and pioneer days.

One afternoon he had been telling some tall bear-hunting stories to a group on the inn porch when a lady asked him whether he had ever eaten any bear meat. His reply was:

"Oh yes Mom, many a time."

She then asked, "What did it taste like, Uncle Billy?"

"Shepherd dog," was the reply.

"Why Uncle Billy," she said, "did you ever eat shepherd dog?"

"No Mom," was the answer.

Although an authority on the manners and ways of more or less primitive life, Uncle Billy knew little of the ways of people in the great outside world. It was doubtful whether he had ever been more than ten miles away from the spot where he came into the world some seventy years before. He had never even seen a railway train, despite the nearness of the railway line, which had been built some years before. Guests at the inn often tried to persuade the old fellow to go down to the railway station at train time and watch the locomotive and cars come in.

Finally Uncle Billy announced one day that on the following day he would go down to the station and watch the train's arrival.

Next day, when the hack returned from the station, sure enough Uncle Billy was right behind it, riding his old white mule. A number of the inn guests flocked out to meet him, eager to hear what a seventy-year-old man would have to say upon first seeing a railway train. A spokesman asked him:

"Did you see the train, Uncle Billy?"

"Shore did," he answered.

"What did you think of it?"

"Not much," the old man replied. "That critter come out of a hole in the groun' a'makin' a turble noise. H'it seen me an' my ole white mule, give a ungodly screech, an' run right smack in another hole in the groun'. Seemed like h'it were plumb scared."

Hog Rifles

Through my years at Dutch Cross I have accumulated a small collection of artifacts made and used by the pioneers who settled our mountain country. Such things as a broadaxe, a froe—used for riving shingles, corded beds, pots, kettles, hand weaves, etc. I derived great pleasure acquiring these things, and several times traded a sketch for such an article.

One glorious day this week I had the supreme pleasure of becoming the owner of a hog rifle I have long been trying to get possession of. It is a muzzle loader, nearly six feet long, with an octagonal barrel an inch in diameter, and it is remarkably accurate. It is great fun shooting it at a mark, and educational too, for it makes one realize better the difficulties the old-timers encountered when they needed to shoot in a hurry.

The next afternoon I was at the store boasting about my rifle to some of the members of the "Jot-'Em-Down Club." An old man in the group spoke up and said:

"Talkin' about that hog rifle makes me think o' my cousin Paul. He got shot las' year with a hog rifle. Didn't hurt him much though. The curious thing about it was there didn't nobody pull no trigger. Howcome h'it were this-a-way. There were a leetle ole log house use'ta stand behind Paul's house. The cover got bad, leaked, an' through the years a lot o' the logs rotted. Even the chimley was bad; rocks had fell off till only about half o' h'it was still a'standin'.

"You know most o' them ole chimleys was built with a arn bar acrost the arch of 'em over the farr hole. Whoever h'it were built this 'un I can't ricollect, but he didn't have no arn bar, an' he had used in place o' h'it a ole hog rifle barl. Paul had looked at that ole rifle barl many a time a'figurin' he'd some day git her out'a thar an' work her up into a good crowbar.

"Finally a day come he didn' have nothin' else on hand, so he tore out that ole chimley, got the barl out, made him a farr in his leetle forge, an' put the barl in to heat. Blowed them bellers till he got her rale hot, found he'd failed to bring his hammer from the shed, so started to git h'it. He got about halfway, an' that there ole rifle barl says, 'ker-pow,' an' put a ball right in the seat of Paul's pants.

"He had to git the doctor man to git that ball out. He didn' do no settin' much fur quite a spell atter that, even had'ta stand when he went to the ration board. All them years that ole rifle barl had been in that chimley loaded, an' nobody knowed h'it."

It has often come to my attention that story-telling is a more or less competitive art. Like as not the person you tell one to will not let the matter rest there but will have a story, probably in much the same vein, to tell you, and he doesn't conceal that he thinks his story a bit better than yours. That certainly proved true on the occasion I am telling about, for another man in the group, Bob Fellowes, spoke up:

"I can tell you-uns another hog rifle story, some-thin' happened over on Stone Mounting where I was raised at. Y'all know how rough an' steep that mounting is, an' most all solid rock. Ain't hardly enough dirt on h'it in most places to raise a parsley bed. H'its hard to figger how them folks over there

manage to make a livin'. Lot of 'em don't even try
to raise no corn. They go down below the mounting
where there's a little mill git's plenty o' corn brought
in from them rich river-bottom farms, an' they
trades for meal an' packs h'it home up that steep
mounting to make their bread.

"I reckon some of you-uns knowed ole Nehemiah
Powers, lived up above Bethel settlement. One time,
bein' out o' meal, he went down to that little mill
to git him some. Carried his rifle gun along with
him, allowin' he might knock over a squirrel or two.

"He was a mischievous ole cuss, kinely like Uncle
Old Flagg. When he got to the mill he got him a
pretty big sack o' meal, him havin' so many to feed,
an' started back up the mounting. H'it were a awful
steep rough path, an' the meal an' the rifle, though
not bad heavy, was awk'ard to carry, an' every now
an' then he'd git tard an' sit an' rest a spell.

"On one o' them rests a young feller lived up near
him, Neal Fulton, overtook him, an' ask him why
he were a'sittin' there. Nehemiah 'lowed he was
sick, bad sick, but nothin' could be done for him,
just let him rest, unless Neal would holp him by
carryin' that meal up the mounting, an' drop h'it
off at home. Neal, bein' a accommodatin' feller,

agreed, throwed the sack over his shoulder, an' got goin' on up that rough trail. Soon as Neal was out o' sight, Nehemiah, carryin' his rifle gun, went a'scramblin' up some near cuts he knowed, an' t'want long a'fore he come to a little clearin' up on top, sat him down on a rock, an' waited.

"When Neal come out o' the woods, sweatin' an' short winded, he seen Nehemiah a'sittin' on that rock. He were a'singin' loud an' bold, his hog rifle gun propped up beside him. An' this is the song he were a'singin':

> I've got a secret I'll never reveal,
> I tote the rifle gun, Neal totes the meal.

Water

Although we have no sidewalks in Dutch Cross, we people who live here are about all sidewalk superintendents by nature. If someone is building a house or barn, even a fence, or maybe just repairing a sled, passers-by are sure to stop and have a look at what is being done.

When I went down for the mail today, I saw a well-boring machine putting down a well at the Methodist Church, so on the way back home I of course had to stop and view the operations going on. I got to thinking about my early days in Dutch Cross when I built my cabin and employed some men to hand-dig a well alongside it. One of the many wonderful things about our mountain country is the fact that one seldom has to bore or dig far under the surface to reach a bountiful supply of water. I never cease to marvel when I come across a fine spring on a mountain top perhaps four or five thousand feet above sea level. In rare cases one may have to bore two hundred or more feet to reach a vein of water, but that is most unusual.

To go back to my well. The men soon got down to a hard blue rock and had to work with a hand drill and dynamite. At some thirty-odd feet down, it got so the men couldn't stand the dynamite fumes, so I let them go and made arrangements with a man who had brought the first well-drilling machine into our neighborhood to come and finish the job.

My cabin is on a bluff about sixty feet above a stream, but at only fifty feet down we reached a bountiful supply of water and ceased drilling operations.

A neighbor, who lived down the river a bit, had need of a new well, and being impressed with the work of the drilling machine, employed the operator to move the outfit down to his place, agreeing to pay him on the customary basis of so much per foot drilled. Joe figured that as my well, put down from sixty feet above the creek bed, was only fifty feet deep, his well, to be put down from only some fifteen feet above the river bed, would probably cost a good bit less than mine had. But alas! That didn't work out.

Day after day the drill ran on and on, deeper and deeper, but no water. Finally, one day at the store someone asked Joe how his well was coming, and whether or not he had hit water. Poor Joe's answer was:

"Lord no, we're down a'most two hundred feet, an' nary a drap. If ever we do hit water, h'it'll be so hot a body cain't drink h'it."

Connivance?

Another story about water came to my ears the other day. It may be somewhat apocryphal, as I seem to have a vague recollection of a very similar story I once heard in another part of the country. However, it's a good tale and, told in the mountain vernacular as I heard it, it has an original flavour all its own. I had gone to see a man about making me some "settin' cheers." I had to wait for him and passed the time talking to his old daddy, who told me the following story:

"Way back yander in ole days when I was a young feller there were a man an' his woman lived up in that leetle flat at the top o' the mounting. That feller were a turble lazy man, never done nothin' much he could git out o' doin', spent most o' his time loaferin' aroun' that leetle store up thar.

But Boys! he had him a woman what didn' care to work. She done near 'bout ever'thin' was done on the place. They had 'em a good leetle farm. The only trouble with it was thar weren't nary bit o' water on h'it closter than a spring 'bout half a mile up the holler behine the house. Fust thing of a mornin' that po' woman would have to take her a bucket, go up that rough holler an' fetch back water. Then of a evenin' a'fore supper thar were the same thing to be done ag'in. H'it got awful old, that traipsin' back an' forth fur water on top o' ever'thin' else she had to do, an' she kep' a'beggin' her man to git some fellers to holp an' dig 'em a well. But no Sir, fur on top o' his laziness that feller were tight too, an' he jus' wouldn' put out nothin'. So the years went by an' that woman had to keep on totin' every drap o' water them people used.

"So h'it went on till one day the woman's sister from Banner's Elk were a'visitin' her, an' that man, like common, was gone to the store fur a long spell. When he finally come in his woman were a'layin' in the bed an' a doctor man from Banner's Elk an' her sister was a'bendin' over her. The doctor man took that feller out on the porch an' tole him the woman had had a bad fall an' hurt her back so bad he were a'feared she wouldn't never walk no more.

"So that feller had to take over, keep all the work done up, wait on his woman, an' all that walkin' twic't a day totin' water. Atter a week o' that what you reckon that man done? Went right out, hired him some work hands an' put 'em to diggin' a well forninst the back door, an' h'it wa'nt long afore they had 'em a good well.

"Every time that doctor man passed that-a-way he'd stop in to see how the woman was a'doin' but h'it seemed like she didn' git no better.

"One day as that man was a'headin' in to the house h'it seemed like he heerd laughin' in thar, an' when he got to the door that doctor met him, his eyes jus' a'shinin', an' says, 'Man, a miracle has happened. Look a'yander.' An' thar was the feller's woman a'standin' on them two feet an' a'walkin'.

"From then on ontil he died out, every time that doctor man passed that house he'd stop in fur a visit, an' him an' that woman would drink water an' laugh big."

Proof Perfect

I have often speculated about what part a good memory plays in the functioning of an active mind, but have never been able to reach a satisfactory conclusion. Now I am more puzzled than ever.

One Sunday afternoon about a year ago when I was down at Sloan Hammond's, I took Mr. and Mrs. Hammond and their daughter over on Dark Mountain to visit Jim McKinney and his sister. Jim and his sister are a unique pair. Jim is eighty-four, tall, slim and looks as though he might have been one of El Greco's models. His sister, Miss Annabelle, can't be far behind in years. They own and live on a fine farm, although it is not a going outfit, they being too advanced in years to keep up farming operations. They have about the only boundary of virgin timber left in the county. Miss Annabelle is a well-educated woman, having had the advantage of a college course. Jim is not an educated man. He has never had an aptitude for book learning. His interest lies largely in watches, jackknives and farm animals. He is famed, however, throughout that countryside for his remarkable memory, his penchant being people's birthdays. I had no sooner been introduced to him than he asked me what my birth date was. Humoring him, I of course told him and promptly forgot all about it.

Yesterday afternoon, it being Sunday, visiting day, I drove down to the Hammonds'. It was such a beautiful day I invited them to go for a drive. Miss Lizzie was delighted and said she had heard that Miss Annabelle was sick, and it would be nice to drive over and see her and take her some things. As we drew near to the McKinneys' house, Miss Lizzie suggested that I ask Jim what my birthday was. It would be interesting to see whether he remembered it. I readily took her suggestion and as soon as we were all seated in the house asked the old man whether he remembered my birth date. Quick as a flash the answer came, and exactly right too.

On our drive back to the Hammonds' house I was marveling over Old Jim's having remembered the birthday of a perfect stranger like me. Uncle Sloan thought it quite impressive but said he could tell me a still more remarkable instance of Old Jim's memory. It took little to launch him into the following tale:

"There's a feller over in Memphis was born an' raised over here in Green Valley, was tryin' to get some kind of a job durin' the war an' found he would have to have a birth certificate. He's got a brother lives here, so he wrote that brother, asked him to get a birth certificate for him. That brother tried but found there wasn't no records they could go by. In such a case a affidavit signed by two reputable people will answer, so the feller's brother went to a old family friend, a much older man, an' asked him would he make such a affidavit. That old man thought an' thought but he couldn't remember the birth date for sure, so didn't want to sign. Finally he thought of Jim McKinney an' said, 'I'll tell you what, let's go see Jim McKinney. If he remembers an' will sign, I will too, 'cause I've never knowed Jim to be wrong on a birthday.'

"The brother and the old family friend went up

to see Jim an' put the question to him. Without a
moment's hesitation Jim answered, '14 June, 1898.'
So they got the affidavit drawed up, an' both men
signed. On the way back that old family friend who
signed the affidavit said:

"'Somethin' just come to me. I know how we can
maybe check on Jim McKinney an' see for sure is
he right. Back in them times when your brother
was born Pap an' me was runnin' the store, an' I
ricollect the day your brother was borned, your pa
come to the store, tole us about the new young-un,
an' bought three yards of red flannel an' a choppin'
axe. Them old account books from the store are in
the loft up at the house. Let's us go there, git 'em
down, turn up that date Jim give us, an' see what's
wrote down for that day.'

"So they done that. Got that old book down,
turned up June 14, 1898, an' there was a entry for
what that boy's daddy had bought that day:

3 yds. Red flannel @ 10¢   .30
1 chopping axe   1.50

Wiping Out a Feud

Density of population can be an enormously important thing to a man's feelings. I dare say the average large city dweller couldn't possibly be happy in a sparsely settled community like Dutch Cross. Conversely, the average Dutch Cross man would be miserable if he had to spend his life amid the hordes of the city.

A good many people are coming from the hot country these days, looking around, and in a growing number of cases, buying a piece of land and building a summer place. This movement is making some of us old-timers uneasy because we don't want to be crowded.

Many of the new people come from Florida, but of course not all of them are interested in buying here. For instance, a certain gentleman met one of

our local men one day last week, and the following
conversation went on between them:

"Sure are a lot of mountains around here."

"Yup."

"A lot of cows too."

"Yup."

"And a lot of ignorant people with nothing much
to say."

"Yup, but h'it'll come a frost soon, an' they'll git
gone back to Floridy."

Some of the newcomers are, however, a distinct
addition to our community.

A few summers ago a personable man, a lawyer
from middle Tennessee, bought a tract of about
twenty-five acres on the back side of Beech Mountain with the idea of building a summer cottage.
The man he bought the land from had long had a
feud with his neighbor who owned the adjoining
land. The feud had to do with the location of the
line fence between them. In fact, that had largely
influenced the sale of the land to the lawyer.

The deed having been executed, recorded, and
payment made, the purchaser came out one morning to look the property over and to give thought
to just what and just where he would build on the

property. He was sitting on the line fence, smoking his pipe and cogitating, when the owner of the adjoining land came up and addressed him:

"Reckon you are the feller bought that Nichols land?"

"Yes Sir, I am," the lawyer replied.

"Well, I just want to let you know you have done bought yourself trouble."

"Why, what's wrong?" the lawyer asked.

"That line fence you are a'sittin' on is eighteen feet over on my land, that's what's wrong."

"Why my friend," said the buyer, "that's no cause for trouble. We'll just change my deed, and I'll meet you here with a couple of men in the morning, and we'll move the fence over twenty-five feet so as to be sure."

It was seven summers ago that the Tennessee lawyer bought that tract of land, and the fence has never been moved an inch. Moreover, those two men are often seen fishing or hunting together.

We could use some more like him.

A Hillbilly Hill Climber

In the long-ago days men sat in drawing rooms, clubs, country stores, at all kinds of man-gathering places, and boasted of their horses. Men still sit in those places and boast, not of their horses, but of their automobiles.

There is a man in our community, George Penney, a huge hulking fellow, with quite a talent as a jack-leg mechanic. During the Second World War George was the proud possessor of an ancient Model T Ford. Gasoline rationing was imposing severe hardship upon most people. George dealt with this difficulty by putting a gallon of kerosene in his tank along with every gallon of gasoline he was able to get. This made starting slow and difficult, and performance poor, but it worked after a fashion.

I was at the post office one day and found George sitting there bragging about his Model T to a group of men and telling how well it ran on a half-kerosene ration. A traveling salesman who was there commented that the car would not have much power on hills.

George's reply to that was that he could drive all the way to the top of Valley Mountain without changing gears. I drew in my breath at this, for the road up Valley Mountain is steep, winding, and about five miles long.

The salesman reached in his pocket, drew out a five-dollar note, and said to George:

"I'll bet you this five you can't go halfway up that mountain without changing gears."

George accepted the bet, put up his five dollars, and said:

"Come on Mister, climb in with me."

With some difficulty George got the motor going and started off with the low-gear pedal pushed down hard. The first half mile or so is almost level, but George kept that low-gear pedal pushed down nearly to the floor boards, untroubled by the engine heat and noise.

"Why don't you put her in high?" yelled the salesman.

"Because that would be changing gears Mister," George said, "and I'd lose the bet."

"OK," said the salesman. "You win. Let's turn around."

Footgear

"Hit weathered" in the night. Winter is really here. The wind is howling around the corners of my house like a banshee. Jack Frost has been at work on the window panes. The bed is warm, the room is cold. With a great exercise of will power I jump out of bed and dash into the warm living room, open the stove drafts, put on a stick of wood; then to the kitchen to put on the coffee, and back to the stove to dress. Out the window my valley is white, clouds of wind-borne snow tearing across the meadows like dust. The outside thermometer at the window shows zero, but I am snug. I have my breakfast alongside the stove. You who live in furnace-heated houses have advantages, but you are missing a lot too. A stove is a bit of trouble, yes, but it has advantages too. Right beside you is the source of heat. You can apply the chill parts of the body closer to the source, and when you get too warm, pull away. Burning hardwood has a wonderful perfume, particularly sassafras, hickory, birch. Into that stove you can empty the ash trays, knock out your pipe, throw letters and trash.

There are some things I must have from the store, so I put on my boots and heavy jacket, and I'm off through six inches of snow. The wind feels as if it has just combed the top of Grandfather Mountain's head, but I haven't far to go.

There was a fine fire roaring in the huge stove in the store, and around it there were sitting half a dozen "Jot-Em-Down Club" members. Among them there was a traveling shoe salesman from Nashville, who had spent the night in the neighborhood. Quite deftly he engineered a conversation to going among the men as to the best kind of footgear a man could wear on such a cold snowy morning.

Various ideas were advanced, until finally the prevailing opinion pretty well settled upon "yarn" (in our vernacular, wool is yarn) socks and well-oiled high leather boots.

Among the group was a man from down the river, Dan Troy. He is a big man with a complexion the

color of a cardinal's cassock. One feels that cold
weather would have little effect upon him. Some
folks say that Dan very successfully carries on certain illicit operations in the woods. It developed
that the footgear discussion was not settled after
all, for Dan had a minority opinion to give. He said:

"Them high leather boots is all right, but you got
to use the right kind of oil on 'em. Cain't nothin'
beat polecat oil. An' another thing Boys, you don't
need no socks. The blood moves aroun' in yore
feet better without no socks. Me, I don't never
wear 'em."

The salesman, with an incredulous look, said:

"Do you mean to say that on a morning like this
you have no socks on your feet?"

"No Sir," Dan said. "I'll jus' show ye."

Dan proceeded to unlace and remove one of his
high leather boots and stuck out a quite unclean,
horny-looking, bare foot. The drummer observed
this with open mouth and popping eyes, and I suppose the rest of us were showing surprise. Then
Bus Hare gummed his chaw, spat and said:

"By golly he's right Boys. He don't need no cold-
weather socks. With that much dirt on 'em, even
'taters won't freeze."

Curtain

When I first started painting a good many years ago, a very fine artist once said to me, "It takes two men to do a good painting, one to actually wield the brush and the other to knock him in the head with a stick when it's done." I suppose it's the same way with writing, speaking, or anything else. I think of the man in front of a church on Sunday morning who asked another man standing there whether the sermon was over, and the reply, "Yes, but the preacher don't know it. He's still talking." In a manner of speaking I have "been hit with a stick," for certain circumstances have come about which call for my leaving Dutch Cross to reside for some months in one of our large cities.

You, my reader, who have followed me thus far, may perhaps think I have overstressed the importance of a bit of salt in the daily living of our lives, to the neglect of that other important ingredient, sugar. The smell of a bit of sweetening goes a long way, as witness one day this Fall when Hobart Turner was making molasses. Several other people were there helping, among them Monroe Brown. The boiling sap was giving off a wonderful smell when a carload of Hobart's in-laws from the low country came driving in. Monroe Brown looked up, saw them and said: "I knowed you could smell them things a long ways, but I never knowed you could smell 'em clean down to Lenoir."

So now I tell you that I have found "sugar" here in Dutch Cross, as well as the "salt." It is my hope that before too long we shall be back again in My Beautiful Valley.